APPLIED
PHYSICS

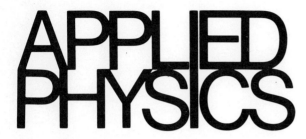

APPLIED PHYSICS

Study Guide/second edition

Paul E. Tippens

Department of Physics
Chairperson, Department of Special Studies
Southern Technical Institute

McGraw-Hill Book Company
Gregg Division

New York	Johannesburg	Panama
St. Louis	London	Paris
Dallas	Madrid	São Paulo
San Francisco	Mexico	Singapore
Auckland	Montreal	Sydney
Bogotá	New Delhi	Tokyo
Düsseldorf		Toronto

Special appreciation is given to Dr. Samuel Nalley and J. W. Tippens for reviewing the material and offering invaluable criticism and advice.

Typing of the basic manuscript and consistency of format and style are due primarily to the efforts of Joyce Scott Tippens.

APPLIED PHYSICS STUDY GUIDE, second edition

ISBN: 0-07-064962-6

1 2 3 4 5 6 7 8 9 0 KPKP 7 8 3 2 1 0 9 8

The editors for this book were Gerald O. Stoner and Mark Haas.
The designer was Roberta Rezk.
The art supervisor was George T. Resch.
The production supervisor was May Kanopka.
It was set in IBM Selectric by Jan Ellis.
Printed and bound by Kingsport Press, Inc.

CONTENTS

PREFACE

This Study Guide is designed for use with APPLIED PHYSICS, second edition, a basic physics textbook published by the McGraw-Hill Book Company, but it is also suited for use with other texts which cover similar concepts. The basic format includes the following items for each unit of study:

1. Contents, a list of major topics
2. Objectives
3. Definitions of major terms
4. Physical concepts
5. True-false questions
6. Multiple-choice questions
7. Completion questions
8. Answers

All the material has been tested in the classroom and revised to effect maximum learning. The Study Guide should be considered as a companion for students. For each unit of instruction, it tells students what is to be learned; it defines the major terms; and then provides opportunities to verify their understanding of physics. Answers are provided at the end of each chapter for all study questions. The beginning student will also need to study the Appendix, which describes a helpful procedure for the solution of physics problems.

The following approach has been found effective for the use of this Study Guide:

1. First, glance over the contents for the unit, and then read the Objectives to see where emphasis is placed.

2. Read the text material thoroughly before each lecture and review the appropriate Definitions from the Study Guide.

3. Test your understanding of basic physics principles by answering the true-false questions. Check your answers in the back of the Study Guide. Read again those parts of the text which pertain to the questions you answered incorrectly.

4. A similar procedure should be followed with the
    multiple choice and completion questions. Refer back
    to the Objectives frequently to maintain the proper
    emphasis.

Another effective use of the Study Guide is to use it in
conjunction with a basic physics text and audio-visual materials to individualize the physics classes. The author has done
this effectively, and student comprehension was comparable
to that experienced for other methods.

                                        Paul E. Tippens

To my mother and father

    for their love and understanding;

To my wife, Joyce,

    for her understanding of love; and

To my children, Scott, Mark, and Blake,

    whom I would love to understand.

CHAPTER 1. INTRODUCTION

CONTENTS

1. What is Physics?
2. The Part Played by Mathematics
3. How to Study Physics

OBJECTIVES

You should be able to:

1. Write definitions of the terms *physics*, *statics*, and *dynamics*.

2. Describe the role played by mathematics as a professional tool for the scientist or engineer.

3. Give two examples which illustrate your conception of the *scientific method* of investigation. In each example identify a workable hypothesis and a scientific conclusion.

DEFINITIONS

<u>Physics</u> - The science which investigates the fundamental concepts of matter, energy, and space and the relationships between them.

<u>Statics</u> - Study of the physical phenomena associated with bodies at rest.

<u>Dynamics</u> - The description of motion and treatment of its causes.

<u>Hypothesis</u> - A statement or equation which is a provisional conjecture to guide further investigation.

<u>Scientific theory</u> - An empirically verified hypothesis which is consistently repeatable and therefore capable of prediction.

TRUE-FALSE QUESTIONS

T F 1. Physics is a field of science that is easily distinguished from other fields such as chemistry or biology.

T F 2. Mathematics serves many purposes, but its main value is to provide a professional tool for the scientist or engineer.

T F 3. All quantities in physics should have specific, measurable definitions.

T F 4. Physics and science are different terms frequently used to describe the same thing and may therefore be used interchangeably.

1

T F 5. Dynamics is a branch of physics devoted to the study of objects at rest or in motion with constant speed.

T F 6. If a problem or definition discussed by an instructor is also in the text, it is better to jot down a reference rather than to take detailed notes.

T F 7. Physics is a quantitative science.

T F 8. Since some information in the text might be misunderstood it is better to wait until after the lecture to read the material.

T F 9. If a workable hypothesis fails only one time in many trials, it still may be incorporated into a scientific law.

T F 10. A good background in mathematics, though desirable, is not really helpful in understanding basic concepts.

ANSWERS TO TRUE-FALSE QUESTIONS

1.	False	5.	False	8.	False
2.	True	6.	True	9.	False
3.	True	7.	True	10.	False
4.	False				

CHAPTER 2. VECTOR MECHANICS

CONTENTS

OBJECTIVES

You should be able to:

1. State three fundamental quantities and their corresponding fundamental units in Bgs and SI units.

2. Convert from one unit to another unit for the same quantity when the appropriate definitions are given.

3. Apply unit analysis to a given physical equation to see if the relationship is dimensionally correct.

4. Define a *vector* quantity and a *scalar* quantity and give examples of each.

5. Determine the x and y components of a given vector by analytical and graphical methods.

6. Find the resultant of two or more vectors by graphical and analytical methods.

7. Determine the magnitude and direction of a vector by analytical and graphical methods when its rectangular components are given.

8. Give a graphic illustration of your understanding of *vector difference*.

DEFINITIONS

Dimension - All physical quantities which can be expressed in the same units have the same physical dimensions. Examples are length, force, and velocity.

Unit - A standard by which a physical quantity is measured, such as a unit of length (m) or a unit of force (N).

Vector quantity - A quantity that is completely specified by its magnitude. For example, 16 km or 144 liters.

Scalar quantity - A quantity that is completely specified by its magnitude. For example, 16 miles or 144 cubic feet.

Displacement - A vector quantity indicating the straight-line distance from a reference point to a known position.

3

Resultant - A resultant force is the single-force vector whose effect
   is the same as that of a number of vectors acting simultaneously.

Component - The projection of a vector on a particular coordinate
   axis, such as the x or y components of a force vector.

Concurrent forces - Forces which intersect at a common point or have
   the same point of application.

PHYSICAL CONCEPTS

1. The polygon method of vector addition: the resultant vector is
    found by drawing each vector to scale, placing the tail end of
    one vector to the tip of the other until all vectors are drawn.
    The resultant is the straight line drawn from the starting point
    to the tip of the last vector (Fig. 2-1).

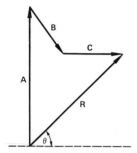

Fig. 2-1.

2. The parallelogram method of vector addition: the resultant of
    two vectors is the diagonal of a parallelogram formed by the two
    vectors as adjacent sides. The direction is away from the common
    origin of the two vectors (Fig. 2-2).

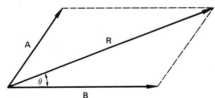

Fig. 2-2.

3. The x and y components of a vector $(\mathbf{R}, \theta)$:

$$R_x = R \cos \theta \qquad R_y = R \sin \theta$$

4

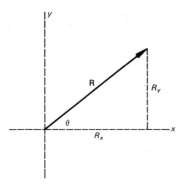

Fig. 2-3.

4. The resultant of two perpendicular vectors (R_x, R_y):

$$R = \sqrt{R_x{}^2 + R_y{}^2} \qquad \tan\theta = \frac{R_y}{R_x}$$

5. The component method of vector addition:

$$R_x = A_x + B_x + C_x + \ldots \qquad R_y = A_y + B_y + C_y + \ldots$$

$$R = \sqrt{R_x{}^2 + R_y{}^2} \qquad \tan\theta = \frac{R_y}{R_x}$$

TRUE-FALSE QUESTIONS

T   F   1.   The fundamental unit for length is the mile.

T   F   2.   The kilogram is equivalent to a mass of 1000 g.

T   F   3.   Only vectors having the same dimensions may be added.

T   F   4.   The difference between two vectors is obtained by adding one vector to the negative of the other.

T   F   5.   The order in which two or more vectors are added does not affect their resultant.

T   F   6.   Given the x component of one vector and the y component of another vector, it is possible to find the resultant of the two vectors mathematically.

T   F   7.   The graphical methods of vector addition are not as accurate as the mathematical method.

T   F   8.   Vector addition can be performed only for concurrent vectors.

5

T F 9. If a boat travels upstream with a speed of 8 km/h in a current whose speed is 3 km/h, the boat's speed relative to the shore is 5 km/h.

T F 10. The x component of the resultant vector is equal to the sum of the x components of the individual vectors.

MULTIPLE-CHOICE QUESTIONS

1. Which of the following is not a fundamental quantity?
   (a) length   (b) force   (c) mass   (d) time

2. The resultant of 10 lb and 15 lb acting in opposite directions on an object is
   (a) 150 lb   (b) 25 lb   (c) 5 lb   (d) 20 lb

3. Which is a scalar quantity?
   (a) velocity   (b) force   (c) speed   (d) displacement

4. A force of 3 N acts perpendicularly to a force of 4 N. Their resultant has a magnitude of
   (a) 12 N   (b) 7 N   (c) 5 N   (d) 1 N

5. Which is a vector quantity?
   (a) volume   (b) time   (c) distance   (d) displacement

6. Given that the units of s, v, a, and t are feet, feet per second, feet per second per second, and seconds, which of the following equations is dimensionally incorrect?
   (a) $s = vt + \frac{1}{2}at$ (b) $2as = v_f^2 - v_0^2$
   (c) $v = v_0 + at$ (d) $s = vt$

7. A force of 16 N is directed 30° north of east. The y component of the force is
   (a) 8 N   (b) 13.8 N   (c) 12 N   (d) 4.8 N

8. A man walks 9 km east and then 12 km north. The magnitude of his resultant displacement is
   (a) 21 km   (b) 15 km   (c) 13 km   (d) 3 km

9. The resultant of the forces in Fig. 2-4 is
   (a) 66.5 N, 222°   (b) 66.5 N, 132°
   (c) 66.5 N, 228°   (d) none of these

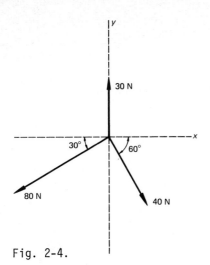

Fig. 2-4.

10. A 20-lb force acts to the left while an 80-lb force acts upward
    and to the right at an angle of 37°. The magnitude of the
    resultant force is
    (a) 80 lb   (b) 70 lb   (c) 65 lb   (d) 100 lb

COMPLETION QUESTIONS

1. If two quantities are to be added or subtracted, they must be of
   the same _____.

2. Three examples of vector quantities are _____,
   _____, and _____.

3. A physical quantity that is completely specified by a number and
   a unit is called a _____.

4. Every vector can be resolved into two perpendicular vectors
   called its _____.

5. A physical quantity that is completely specified by a number,
   a unit, and a direction is called a _____.

6. In the _____ method of vector addition, the tail of
   one vector is connected to the tip of another until all vectors
   have been represented.

7. The _____ is a single force whose effect is
   the same as that of a given set of concurrent forces.

8. In the component method, the x component of the resultant vector
   is equal to the sum of the _____ of each vector.

9. Forces which intersect at a common point or have the same point
   of application are said to be _____.

7

10. The difference between two vectors is obtained by adding one vector to the _____ of the other.

ANSWERS TO TRUE-FALSE, MULTIPLE CHOICE, AND COMPLETION QUESTIONS

1.	False	1.	b	1.	dimensions
2.	True	2.	c	2.	displacement, velocity, force
3.	True	3.	c	3.	scalar
4.	True	4.	c	4.	components
5.	True	5.	d	5.	vector
6.	False	6.	a	6.	polygon
7.	True	7.	a	7.	resultant force
8.	True	8.	b	8.	x components
9.	True	9.	d	9.	concurrent
10.	True	10.	c	10.	negative

CHAPTER 3. TRANSLATIONAL EQUILIBRIUM

CONTENTS

OBJECTIVES

You should be able to:

1. Experimentally demonstrate your understanding of Newton's first law of motion.

2. Give at least two examples with appropriate discussion to illustrate your understanding of Newton's third law of motion.

3. State the first condition for equilibrium both verbally and mathematically, give a physical example, and demonstrate graphically that the first condition is satisfied.

4. Construct a free-body diagram representing all forces acting on an object which is in translational equilibrium.

5. Apply the first condition of equilibrium to set up two equations involving components of given vectors along the major axes.

6. Solve for unknown forces by applying the first condition for equilibrium.

7. Define the forces of kinetic friction and static friction and suggest a means of measuring them.

8. Design an experiment which will determine the coefficients of static and kinetic friction for two given surfaces.

9. Write a theoretical relationship for calculating frictional forces and apply this relationship to the solution of general force problems involving the use of vectors.

10. Define the *limiting angle of repose* for two surfaces and suggest a procedure for its measurement.

DEFINITIONS

Inertia - A property of matter which represents its resistance to any change in its state of rest or motion.

Reaction force - The equal and opposite force which, according to
Newton's third law, results when any force is applied to a
material.

Equilibrium - A condition in which all forces or tendencies are
exactly counterbalanced or neutralized by equal and opposite
forces and tendencies. Translational equilibrium exists when the
sum of all forces acting on a body is zero.

Equilibrant - A force vector which is equal in magnitude to the resultant force but opposite in direction.

Free-body diagram - A vector diagram depicting every force that acts
on a body and labeling the components of each force opposite and
adjacent to known angles.

Friction - Resistive forces between two surfaces in contact which
oppose actual or impending motion. The force of static friction
exists when motion is impending but no sliding occurs. The force
of kinetic friction exists between two surfaces in relative
motion.

Coefficient of friction - The ratio of the magnitude of a friction
force to the normal force between two surfaces when motion is
actual or impending.

Normal force - A supporting force exerted perpendicular to the plane
of motion or support.

Angle of repose - The angle of inclination for which static friction
is just overcome. The angle whose tangent is equal to the
coefficient of static friction.

PHYSICAL CONCEPTS

1. Free-body diagrams: from the conditions of the problem a neat
    sketch is drawn and all known quantities are labeled. Then a
    force diagram indicating all forces and their components is con-
    structed. All information such as that given in Fig. 3-1 should
    be a part of the diagram.

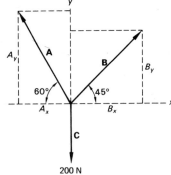

Fig. 3-1.

10

2. Translational equilibrium: a body in translational equilibrium has no resultant force acting on it. In such cases, the sum of all the x components is zero, and the sum of all the y components is zero. This is known as the first condition for equilibrium and is written

$$\overline{R_x = \Sigma F_x = 0} \qquad \overline{R_y = \Sigma F_y = 0}$$

Applying these conditions to Fig. 3-1, for example, we obtain two equations in two unknowns:

$$B \cos 45° - A \cos 60° = 0$$

$$B \sin 45° + A \sin 60° - 200 \text{ N} = 0$$

These equations can be solved to find A and B.

3. Static friction exists between two surfaces when motion is impending; kinetic friction occurs when the two surfaces are in relative motion. In either case, the friction forces are proportional to the normal force. They are given by

$$\overline{F_s = \mu_s N} \qquad \overline{F_K = \mu_K N}$$

These forces must often be considered in equilibrium problems.

TRUE-FALSE QUESTIONS

T F 1. A moving body cannot be in equilibrium.

T F 2. In equilibrium problems, the normal force will always equal the weight of a body.

T F 3. According to Newton's first law of motion, every action force has an equal but opposite reaction force.

T F 4. Action and reaction forces do not neutralize each other because they act on different objects.

T F 5. Newton's first law of motion is also referred to as the *law of inertia*.

T F 6. Under a condition of equilibrium, any one of the forces acting on an object is the equilibrant of the vector sum of all the other forces.

T F 7. Static friction does not exist until motion is impending.

T F 8. The maximum force of static friction is directly proportional to the weight of a body.

T F 9. The parallel force required to move an object over a surface at constant speed is equal to the magnitude of the
force of kinetic friction.

T F 10. The higher the coefficient of friction between two surfaces, the higher the angle of repose for those surfaces
will be.

MULTIPLE-CHOICE QUESTIONS

1. If two vertical ropes are used to support a 20-N weight, the
tension in each rope must be
(a) 20 N   (b) 40 N   (c) 10 N   (d) 30 N

2. A rope attached to a post in the ground is pulled horizontally
with a force of 80 lb. The pole pulls back with a force of
(a) 40 lb   (b) 80 lb   (c) 100 lb   (d) 160 lb

3. Which of the following cannot apply for a body in translational
equilibrium?
(a) $\Sigma F_x = 0$ (b) constant speed
(c) increasing speed   (d) $\Sigma F_y = 0$

4. Find the tension in the cable for the arrangement in Fig. 3-2.
(a) 72.1 N   (b) 67.3N   (c) 50.5 N   (d) 37.2 N

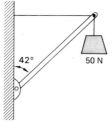

42°   50 N

Fig. 3-2. Find the cable tension.

5. A 40-N block is supported by two ropes. One rope is horizontal,
and the other makes an angle of 30° with the ceiling. The tension
in the rope attached to the ceiling is approximately
(a) 80 N   (b) 34.6 N   (c) 40 N   (d) 46.2 N

6. A 200-lb block is at rest on a 37° inclined plane. The normal
force exerted by the plane is approximately
(a) 120 lb   (b) 200 lb   (c) 160 lb   (d) 100 lb

7. A 60-lb block rests on a smooth horizontal surface. The horizontal force which just starts the block moving is found to be 30 lb.
Which of the following is true for this situation?
(a) $\mu_K = 0.5$ (b) $\mu_s = 0.5$ (c) $\mu_s = 0.18$ (d) $F_K = 30$ lb

8. A 40-N block slides down a board with constant speed when the angle of elevation is 30°. Which of the following is *not* true for this situation?
   (a) $\tan 30 = \mu_K$ (b) $F_K = 20$ N
   (c) $F_K = 34.6$ N   (d) $\mu_K = 0.577$

9. It is easier to pull a sled at an angle than it is to push a sled at an angle because of a
   (a) lower normal force   (b) lower weight
   (c) higher normal force   (d) mechanical advantage

10. If $\mu_K = 0.1$, the force required to push a 20-N sled up a 40° incline with constant speed is approximately
    (a) 26.1 N   (b) 14.4 N   (c) 15.3 N   (d) 31.1 N

COMPLETION QUESTIONS

1. "To every action there must be an equal and opposite reaction." This statement is known as _____.

2. The force of _____ is the tangential force between two surfaces which are in relative motion.

3. A body is in _____ if the vector sum of all forces acting on it is _____.

4. A _____ is used to sketch the forces acting on an object before applying the first condition for equilibrium.

5. In drawing free-body diagrams, it is usually best to choose the x axis _____ the plane of motion and the y axis _____ the plane of motion.

6. The maximum force of static friction is equal to the product of the normal force and _____.

7. A body at rest remains at rest and a body in motion with constant speed remains in motion at constant speed unless _____ _____.

8. If $\mu_K = 0.2$ and $\mu_S = 0.4$, the force required to move a 50-lb block with constant speed is _____.

9. The vector which is equal in magnitude to the resultant vector but opposite in direction is called the _____.

10. The _____ is the limiting angle of inclination for which sliding just begins.

ANSWERS TO TRUE-FALSE, MULTIPLE CHOICE, AND COMPLETION QUESTIONS

1.	False	1.	c	1.	Newton's third law
2.	False	2.	b	2.	kinetic friction
3.	False	3.	c	3.	equilibrium, zero
4.	True	4.	b	4.	free-body diagram
5.	True	5.	a	5.	along, normal to
6.	True	6.	c	6.	the coefficient of static
7.	False	7.	b		friction
8.	False	8.	c	7.	acted on by a resultant force
9.	True	9.	a	8.	10 lb
10.	True	10.	b	9.	equilibrant
				10.	angle of repose

CHAPTER 4. ROTATIONAL EQUILIBRIUM

CONTENTS

OBJECTIVES

You should be able to:

1. State the second condition for equilibrium both verbally and mathematically.

2. Give graphic representations of physical cases where (a) only the first condition for equilibrium is satisfied, (b) only the second condition is satisfied, (c) both conditions are satisfied, and (d) neither condition is satisfied.

3. State whether the resulting torque is positive or negative by convention when given a group of sketches in which a force is applied to an extended object pivoted at some point.

4. Calculate the resultant torque about any point given the magnitude and position of forces applied to an extended object.

5. Solve for unknown forces by applying the first and/or the second condition for equilibrium.

6. Define the *center of gravity* and, given a specific example, determine its location either mathematically or experimentally.

7. Give at least four examples of the practical application of the principle of torque.

8. Be able to design an experiment to determine an unknown weight using a meterstick, a support, and a known weight.

DEFINITIONS

Moment arm - The perpendicular distance from the axis of rotation to the line of action of a force.

Axis of rotation - A chosen point about which forces tend to cause rotation. Once the axis is chosen, the sum of torques about the axis will be zero for rotational equilibrium.

Torque - The product of the magnitude of a force and the perpendicular distance from the line of action of the force to a point which is the center of rotation induced by that force.

15

<u>Noncurrent forces</u> - Forces which do not have a common point of inter-
section or application.

<u>Rotational equilibrium</u> - An object is said to be in rotational equi-
librium when the sum of all the torques about a chosen axis is
zero.

<u>Center of gravity</u> - The point through which the resultant force due
to gravity acts no matter how an object is oriented. For application to rotation problems, all the object's weight may be
considered to act at this point.

PHYSICAL CONCEPTS

1. The moment of force, or torque, about an axis is the product of
the magnitude of that force and its moment arm:

$$Torque = Force \times Moment\ arm$$

$$\underline{L = Fr}$$

It is positive if
it tends to pro- $\oplus$ ccw
duce counterclock-
wise motion and $\ominus$ cw
negative if clock-
wise.

2. The resultant torque about a particular axis A is the algebraic
sum of the torques produced by each force. The signs are determined by the above convention:

$$L_A = \Sigma L_A = F_1 r_1 + F_2 r_2 + F_3 r_3 + \ldots$$

3. Rotational equilibrium: a body in rotational equilibrium has no
resultant torque acting on it. In such cases, the sum of all
the torques about any axis must equal zero. The axis may be
chosen anywhere because the system is not tending to rotate about
any point. This is called the second condition for equilibrium
and may be written

$$\Sigma L = 0 \qquad the\ sum\ of\ all\ torques\ about\ any\ point\ is\ zero$$

4. Total equilibrium exists when the first and second conditions
are satisfied. In such cases, three independent equations can
be written:

(a) $\Sigma F_x = 0$ (b) $\Sigma F_y = 0$ (c) $\Sigma L = 0$

By writing these equations for a given situation, unknown forces,
distances, or torques can be found.

TRUE-FALSE QUESTIONS

T   F   1. When considering only concurrent forces, we do not need
to calculate torques.

T F 2. If an object is suspended from the ceiling by a rope attached to its center of gravity, the system will attain equilibrium.

T F 3. The moment arm is the distance from the point of application of a force to the axis of rotation.

T F 4. When a force tends to cause clockwise rotation, it produces a positive torque by convention.

T F 5. In applying the second condition for equilibrium, the axis of rotation may be chosen for convenience.

T F 6. The center of gravity of a body is always at the geometrical center of the body.

T F 7. In applying the second condition for equilibrium, it is acceptable to equate the clockwise torques about any axis to the counterclockwise torques about the same axis.

T F 8. In computing the resultant torque, the axis of rotation may be chosen for convenience.

T F 9. The unit of torque in the metric system is the newton-meter.

T F 10. The net torque will be the same if a force is doubled but moved to a point halfway to the axis of rotation.

MULTIPLE-CHOICE QUESTIONS

1. To apply the second condition for equilibrium, the axis of rotation
   (a) must be at the center of the body
   (b) must be at one end
   (c) may be chosen anywhere
   (d) must be at the center of gravity

2. In order to compute torque, one must know
   (a) the force magnitude   (b) the moment arm
   (c) both of these   (d) neither of these

3. A rope is wrapped in a clockwise direction around a 12-in.-diameter axle. If a force of 20 lb is exerted on the rope, what is the resultant torque?
   (a) -20 lb·ft   (b) +20 lb·ft   (c) -10 lb·ft   (d) 10 lb·ft

4. A 60-lb boy sits on the left end of a 12-ft seesaw, and a 40-lb boy sits on the right end. The resultant torque about the center is approximately
   (a) -120 lb·ft (b) +20 lb·ft   (c) +120 lb·ft (d) 240 lb·ft

5. Which of the following is not a unit of torque?
   (a) lb·ft   (b) kg·N   (c) N·m   (d) lb·in.

17

6. If the resultant of a set of concurrent forces is zero, the sum
   of the torques
   (a) is also zero   (b) may or may not be zero
   (c) is not zero   (d) depends on the axis of rotation

7. A 20-lb uniform board is 16 ft long and is supported at a point
   6 ft from the right end. The upward force which must be exerted
   at the left end to balance the system is approximately
   (a) 4 lb   (b) 2 lb   (c) 3.6 lb   (d) 5 lb

8. A rope is wrapped around a 16-in. diameter drum in a counterclockwise direction. What force must be exerted on the rope to give
   a torque of 120 lb·ft?
   (a) 90 lb   (b) 75 lb   (c) 200 lb   (d) 180 lb

9. A girl and a boy carry a sack weighing 40 N on a pole between
   them. If the pole is 6 m long and the load is 2 m from the girl,
   what force does the boy exert?
   (a) 13.3 N   (b) 26.7 N   (c) 40 N   (d) 80 N

10. The boom in Fig. 4-1 is 2 m long and weighs 100 N. If the 800-N
    load is suspended 50 cm from the end, the cable tension is
    approximately
    (a) 310 N   (b) 352 N   (c) 424 N   (d) 512 N

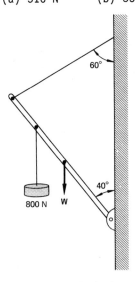

Fig. 4-1. Find the cable tension.

COMPLETION QUESTIONS

1. The _____ distance from the line of
   action of a force to the point of rotation is known as the
   _____.

18

2. The _____ of a body is that point at which all the weight of the body may be considered to be concentrated.

3. The second condition for equilibrium states that the sum of all the _____ acting on an object must be _____.

4. By convention, torques which tend to cause clockwise motion are considered _____, and those which tend to cause counterclockwise motion are considered _____.

5. If the line of action of a force passes through the axis of rotation, the moment arm is _____.

6. In problems involving nonconcurrent forces, both the resultant _____ and the resultant _____ must be zero.

7. The unit for moment of force in the mks system is the _____.

8. The center of gravity of a regular solid of uniform density, such as a sphere or cube, is located at _____.

9. An alternate way of computing the moment of a force is to resolve the force into parallel and perpendicular components and _____.

10. Three tools which utilize the principle of torque are _____, _____, and _____.

ANSWERS TO TRUE-FALSE, MULTIPLE CHOICE, AND COMPLETION QUESTIONS

1. True	1. c	1. perpendicular, moment arm
2. True	2. c	2. center of gravity
3. False	3. c	3. torques, zero
4. False	4. c	4. negative, positive
5. True	5. b	5. zero
6. False	6. a	6. force, torque
7. True	7. a	7. newton-meter
8. False	8. d	8. the geometric center
9. True	9. a	9. sum the torques due to each
10. True	10. c	component
		10. a wheelbarrow, wrench, and pliers

CHAPTER 5.   ACCELERATION

CONTENTS

OBJECTIVES

You should be able to:

1. Distinguish between (a) displacement and distance, (b) speed and velocity, and (c) average speed and instantaneous speed.

2. Relate average speed to distance traveled and time elapsed in order to solve practical problems involving these parameters.

3. State two conditions which are necessary if motion is to be described as *uniformly accelerated motion*.

4. Define *acceleration* and *average speed* and suggest means for measuring them.

5. Write four general equations involving distance, initial velocity, final velocity, acceleration, and time.

6. Solve for any two of the five parameters mentioned in Objective 5 when the other three are given.

7. Write the value of the acceleration due to gravity (near the surface of the earth) in metric and Bgs units.

8. Predict the position and velocity at specific times for an object dropped from rest or projected upward with an initial velocity.

9. Perform a unit analysis for each boxed equation in the chapter to prove that they are dimensionally correct.

DEFINITIONS

Constant speed - An object which covers the same distances in each successive unit of time is said to move with constant speed. The magnitude of such speed is computed by calculating the ratio of distance to time.

Average speed - The average speed for a specific distance is calculated by taking the ratio of that distance to the time elapsed.

Instantaneous speed - A scalar quantity representing the speed at the
    instant an object is at a specific point. It is the time rate of
    change of distance.

Velocity - A vector quantity denoting the time rate of change in
    displacement. A statement of velocity includes a scalar magni-
    tude, expressed in units of length divided by time, and a direc-
    tion relative to some point of reference.

Instantaneous velocity - The velocity at a particular instant and at
    a particular point in its path.

Acceleration - A vector quantity representing the time rate of change
    in velocity. The scalar magnitude has units of length per unit
    per unit time.

Uniformly accelerated motion - Motion in a straight line in which the
    speed changes at a constant rate. Since there is no change in
    direction, such constant acceleration can be computed by a scalar
    equation dividing the change in speed by the time elapsed.

Acceleration due to gravity - The acceleration with which an object
    falls at a specific location in a gravitational field. At sea
    level on the earth, the value is 32.17 ft/s^2 or 9.81 m/s^2.

PHYSICAL CONCEPTS

1. The definitions of velocity and acceleration result in the estab-
    lishment of four basic equations involving uniformly accelerated
    motion:

$$s = \frac{\overline{v_0 + v_f}}{2} t$$

$$v_f = v_0 + at$$

$$s = v_0 t + \tfrac{1}{2}at^2$$

$$2as = v_f^2 - v_0^2$$

Given any three of the five
parameters $(v_0, v_f, a, s,$ or $t)$,
the other two can be determined
from one of these equations.

2. To solve acceleration problems read the problem with a view to
    establishing the three given parameters and the two which are
    unknown. You might set up columns like

Given: $a = 4$ m/s^2 Find: $v_f = ?$
        $s = 500$ m
        $t = 20$ s $v_0 = ?$

This procedure helps you choose the appropriate equation.
Remember to choose a direction as positive and to apply it con-
sistently throughout the problem.

3. Gravitational acceleration: problems involving gravitational acceleration can be solved like other acceleration problems. In this case, one of the parameters is known in advance to be

$$a = g = 9.8 \text{ m/s}^2 \text{ or } 32 \text{ ft/s}^2$$

The sign of the gravitational acceleration is + or - depending on whether you choose up or down as the positive direction.

TRUE-FALSE QUESTION

T F 1. An object in motion can have a constant velocity only if it moves in a straight path.

T F 2. An object falling freely from rest near the surface of the earth falls a distance of 32 ft by the end of the first second.

T F 3. In a vacuum, all bodies fall with the same velocity.

T F 4. If an object's velocity is decreasing constantly, it will always have a negative acceleration.

T F 5. An object thrown downward in a gravitational field has the same acceleration as one dropped from rest.

T F 6. If an object has an acceleration of 8 m/s^2, every second its distance will increase by 8 m.

T F 7. For a ball thrown vertically upward, its upward motion with respect to position and velocity is just the reverse of its downward motion.

T F 8. The velocity and position of a free-falling body after 2s are numerically the same.

T F 9. In the absence of friction, all bodies, large or small, heavy or light, fall to the earth with the same acceleration.

T F 10. If any two of the parameters v_0 v_f, a, s, and t are given, the other three can be calculated from derived equations.

MULTIPLE-CHOICE QUESTIONS

1. An object falls freely from rest. Its position after 2 s is how far below the point of release?
   (a) 32 ft   (b) 64 ft   (c) 96 ft   (d) 48 ft

2. If the initial velocity, the distance traveled, and the time elapsed are known, which equation would you use to calculate the acceleration?
(a) $s = vt$ (b) $s = v_0t + \frac{1}{2}at^2$
(c) $v_f = v_0 + at$ (d) $2as = v_f - v_0$

3. The algebraic sign of acceleration depends on
(a) the choice of direction
(b) whether an object is speeding up or slowing down
(c) the sign of the final velocity
(d) the position of the object

4. An object traveling initially at 24 ft/s slows to 12 ft/s in 3 s. Its acceleration is
(a) 4 ft/s^2 (b) -4 ft/s   (c) -4 ft/s^2 (d) -8 ft/s^2

5. The distance traveled by the object in the previous problem is
(a) 48 ft   (b) 66 ft   (c) 98 ft   (d) 54 ft

6. An object is thrown downward with an initial velocity of 32 ft/s. Its velocity after 3 s is
(a) 102 ft/s   (b) 96 ft/s   (c) 80 ft/s   (d) 128 ft/s

7. A car accelerates from rest at 4 m/s^2. How far will it travel in 4 s?
(a) 32 m   (b) 19.6 m   (c) 78.4 m   (d) 94.4 m

8. An arrow is shot vertically upward with an initial velocity of 96 ft/s. It will first come to a stop in
(a) 4 s   (b) 2 s   (c) 3 s   (d) 6 s

9. An object is projected upward with an initial speed of 64 ft/s. What will be its position above the point of release after 3 s?
(a) 48 ft   (b) 16 ft   (c) 32 ft   (d) 64 ft

10. A car accelerates for 10 s at 6 m/s^2. What is its final speed if its initial speed was 4 m/s?
(a) 60 m/s   (b) 64 m/s   (c) 34 m/s   (d) 30 m/s

COMPLETION QUESTIONS

1. The total distance traveled divided by the time elapsed is a measure of _____.

2. _____ is motion in a straight line in which the speed changes at a constant rate.

3. At least _____ of the following parameters must be known to find the other two: _____, _____, _____, _____, and _____.

4. The final speed is equal to the initial speed plus _____ _____.

23

5. In the absence of friction, all objects fall to the earth with the same _____ independently of size or weight.

6. A body which has a continually increasing negative velocity has a _____ acceleration.

7. The acceleration due to gravity near the earth is 32 _____ or _____ m/s^2.

8. If the upward direction is chosen as positive, a negative distance s indicates that the final position is _____ _____.

9. The distances traveled by an object dropped from rest after 1, 2, and 3 s are _____ ft, _____ m, and _____ ft, respectively.

10. An acceleration of 4 ft/s^2 means that every _____ the velocity increases by _____.

ANSWERS TO TRUE-FALSE, MULTIPLE CHOICE, AND COMPLETION QUESTIONS

1.	True	1.	b	1.	average speed
2.	False	2.	b	2.	uniformly accelerated motion
3.	False	3.	a	3.	three; v_f, v_0, a, t, and s
4.	False	4.	c	4.	the change in speed
5.	True	5.	d	5.	acceleration
6.	False	6.	d	6.	negative
7.	True	7.	a	7.	ft/s^2, 9.8
8.	True	8.	c	8.	below the point of release
9.	True	9.	a	9.	16, 19.6, 144
10.	False	10.	b	10.	second, 4 ft/s

CHAPTER 6. PROJECTILE MOTION

CONTENTS

OBJECTIVES

You should be able to:

1. Explain graphically how the motion of a horizontally projected ball compares with that of a ball dropped from rest.

2. Explain with diagrams how the vertical motion of a projectile fired at any angle is similar to the motion of a ball projected vertically.

3. Demonstrate that all boxed equations appearing in this chapter are dimensionally correct.

4. Predict the position and velocity of a projectile as a function of time when its initial position and velocity are given.

5. Determine the range, the maximum height, and the time of flight for a missile when the initial speed and angle of projection are given.

DEFINITIONS

Projectile - An object which is given an initial velocity and then allowed to move freely under the influence of gravity.

Trajectory - The path followed by a projectile.

Range - The horizontal distance traveled by a projectile from the point of release to the point of final impact.

PHYSICAL CONCEPTS

The key to problems involving projectile motion is to treat the horizontal motion and the vertical motion separately. Most projectile problems are solved using the following approach:

1. Resolve the initial velocity v_0 into its x and y components:

$$\boxed{v_{0x} = v_0 \cos \theta} \qquad \boxed{v_{0y} = v_0 \sin \theta}$$

2. The horizontal and vertical components of its position at any instant are given by

$$x = v_{0x}t \qquad y = v_{0y}t + \tfrac{1}{2}gt^2$$

3. The horizontal and vertical components of its velocity at any instant are given by

$$v_x = v_0 \qquad v_y = v_0 + gt$$

4. The final position and velocity can then be obtained from their components.

The important point to remember in applying these equations is to be consistent throughout with units and sign conversion.

TRUE-FALSE QUESTIONS

T   F   1.   The motion of a projectile fired at an angle is an example of uniformly accelerated motion.

T   F   2.   The resultant force acting on a projectile is its weight.

T   F   3.   A projectile fired horizontally will strike the ground in the same time as one dropped vertically from the same position if we neglect the effects of air resistance.

T   F   4.   A projectile launched into space at any angle will have a constant horizontal velocity.

T   F   5.   The horizontal range is greatest when the angle of projection is 45°.

T   F   6.   The vertical motion of a projectile is uniformly accelerated motion.

T   F   7.   The range of a projectile depends only on its initial speed.

T   F   8.   A horizontally fired projectile will drop 32 ft during the first second.

T   F   9.   If an apple drops from a tree at the same instant a projectile is fired toward it from the ground, they will still collide in the air.

T   F   10.   When a projectile is fired at a 45° angle, its maximum height will equal its range.

MULTIPLE-CHOICE QUESTIONS

1. The acceleration of a projectile is
   (a) g (b) $-g$ (c) 0
   (d) dependent on its initial speed

2. A projectile is fired horizontally with an initial speed of 20
   m/s. Its horizontal speed 3 s later is
   (a) 20 m/s   (b) 60 m/s   (c) 6.67 m/s   (d) 29.4 m/s

3. The vertical speed of the above projectile after 3 s is
   approximately
   (a) 60 m/s   (b) 9.8 m/s   (c) 29.4 m/s   (d) 20 m/s

4. A cannonball is projected horizontally with a velocity of 1200
   ft/s from the top of a cliff 128 ft high. It will strike the
   water below in approximately
   (a) 8 s   (b) 2.83 s   (c) 0.1 s   (d) 9.38 s

5. In Problem 4, the horizontal range is approximately
   (a) 3396 ft   (b) 1200 ft   (c) 938 ft   (d) 9600 ft

6. A projectile is fired at an angle of 30° with an initial speed of
   640 ft/s. The time to reach its maximum height is approximately
   (a) 17.3 s   (b) 20 s   (c) 5 s   (d) 10 s

7. In the above problem, the horizontal range is
   (a) 5542 ft   (b) 11,084 ft   (c) 3200 ft   (d) 6400 ft

8. A projectile is fired at an angle of 37° with an initial speed
   of 100 m/s. What is the approximate vertical component of its
   velocity after 2 s?
   (a) 60 m/s   (b) 40 m/s   (c) 80 m/s   (d) 100 m/s

9. In Problem 8, the position above the ground after 3 s is approximately
   (a) 200 m   (b) 140 m   (c) 136 m   (d) 120 m

10. Which of the following projection angles will result in the
    greatest range?
    (a) 20°   (b) 37°   (c) 48°   (d) 60°

COMPLETION QUESTIONS

1. A projectile is an object launched into space under the influence
   of _____ only.

2. In working with trajectories, it is easier to treat the
   _____ and the _____ motions
   separately.

3. The vertical component of the velocity of a projectile as a
   function of time is calculated from _____.

4. The vertical position of a projectile as a function of time is given by _____.

5. The range of a projectile can be calculated from _____.

6. Projectiles fired upward, downward, or at an angle all have the same _____.

7. The only force acting on a projectile is its _____.

8. The maximum height of a projectile may be found by dividing the _____ component of the initial _____ by the _____.

9. For projectile motion, the _____ component of the _____ is constant.

10. The vertical position of a projectile fired horizontally can be calculated from _____.

ANSWERS TO TRUE-FALSE, MULTIPLE CHOICE, AND COMPLETION QUESTIONS

1. False	1. b	1. gravity
2. True	2. a	2. horizontal, vertical
3. True	3. c	3. $v_y = v_{0y} + \frac{1}{2}gt^2$
4. True	4. b	4. $y = v_{0y}t + \frac{1}{2}gt^2$
5. True	5. a	5. $x = v_{0x}t$
6. True	6. d	6. acceleration
7. False	7. b	7. weight
8. False	8. b	8. vertical, velocity, acceleration of gravity
9. True	9. c	9. horizontal, velocity
10. False	10. c	10. $y = \frac{1}{2}gt^2$

CHAPTER 7.   NEWTON'S SECOND LAW

CONTENTS

OBJECTIVES

You should be able to:

1. Write Newton's second law of motion in your own words and as a
    mathematical statement.

2. Write the units of force, mass, and acceleration in SI and Bgs
    units.

3. Define the units *newton* and *slug* and be able to explain why they
    are said to be *derived* units rather than *fundamental* units.

4. Describe or conduct experiments which would show the variations
    in acceleration produced by a change in the applied force or by
    a change in the accelerated mass.

5. Demonstrate by definition and example your understanding of the
    distinction between *mass* and *weight*.

6. Determine mass from weight or weight from mass at a point where
    the acceleration due to gravity is known.

7. Draw a free-body diagram for a body or system of bodies in motion
    with constant acceleration, set the resultant force equal to the
    total mass times the acceleration, and solve for unknown param-
    eters.

DEFINITIONS

Newton's second law of motion - Whenever an unbalanced force acts on
    a body, it produces an acceleration in the direction of the
    force. This acceleration is directly proportional to the force
    and inversely proportional to the mass of the body.

Mass - A physical measure of the inertia of a body which is the
    constant ratio of an applied force to the acceleration it pro-
    duces. In a gravitational field, the mass of an object is the
    constant ratio of its weight to the gravitational acceleration.

Weight - The force with which a body is attracted to the earth; its
    magnitude is equal to the product of the mass of the body and
    the acceleration due to gravity. Weight, therefore, varies with
    the value for gravitational acceleration.

Newton - The resultant force required to give a 1-kg mass an acceler-
    ation of 1 m/s^2.

Slug - The mass to which a resultant force of 1 lb will give an
    acceleration of 1 ft/s^2.

PHYSICAL CONCEPTS

1. Newton's second law of motion relates force to mass and acceler-
    ation according to the formula

    $$Force = mass \times acceleration$$

    $$F = ma \qquad m = \frac{F}{g} \qquad a = \frac{F}{m}$$

    In SI units: $1N = (1 \text{ kg})(1 \text{ m/s}^2)$

    In Bgs units: $1 \text{ lb} = (1 \text{ slug})(1 \text{ ft/s}^2)$

2. Weight is the force due to a particular acceleration g. Thus
    weight W is related to mass m by Newton's second law:

    $$W = mg \qquad m = \frac{F}{g} \qquad g = 9.8 \text{ m/s}^2 \text{ or } 32 \text{ ft/s}^2$$

    For example, a mass of 1 kg has a weight of 9.8 N. A weight of
    1 lb has a mass of 1/32 slug. In a given problem you must deter-
    mine if weight or mass is given. Then you must determine what is
    needed in an equation. Conversions of mass to weight and weight
    to mass are common.

3. Application of Newton's second law:

    (a) Construct a free-body diagram for each body undergoing an
        acceleration. Indicate on this diagram the direction of
        positive acceleration.

    (b) Determine an expression for the net resultant force on a
        body or a system of bodies.

    (c) Set the above expression equal to the total mass of the
        system multiplied by the acceleration of the system.

    (d) Solve the resulting equation for the unknown quantity.

    Several examples of this procedure are given in the text.

30

TRUE-FALSE QUESTIONS

T   F   1.   The kilogram is the metric unit of weight.

T   F   2.   The mass of an object on the moon is the same as its
              mass on earth.

T   F   3.   The British unit for mass is the slug.

T   F   4.   Newton's second law of motion is strictly true only in
              the absence of friction forces.

T   F   5.   The mass of a body is dependent upon the acceleration due
              to gravity.

T   F   6.   The acceleration an object receives is proportional to
              the applied force, the constant of proportionality being
              the reciprocal of its mass.

T   F   7.   The weight of an object is equal to the product of its
              mass and the gravitational acceleration.

T   F   8.   Newton's second law of motion applies either to a system
              of bodies moved together as a whole or to any body which
              is a part of such a system.

T   F   9.   The weight of a body whose mass is 1 slug is equal to
              approximately 32 lb.

T   F   10.   The weight of a 9.8-kg body is 1 N.

MULTIPLE-CHOICE QUESTIONS

1. The mass of an 80-lb sled is
   (a) 5 slugs   (b) 2.5 slugs   (c) 2.5 kg   (d) 256 slugs

2. The weight of a 10-kg block is
   (a) 98 N   (b) 9.8 N   (c) 10 N   (d) 0.98 N

3. What acceleration will a force at 40 N impart to a mass of 5 kg?
   (a) 8 m/s   (b) 200 m/s^2 (c) 8 m/s^2 (d) 8 cm/s^2

4. What resultant force will give a 64-lb object an acceleration of
   6 ft/s^2?
   (a) 384 lb   (b) 10.7 lb   (c) 12 slug   (d) 12 lb

5. When a 1-N force acts on a 1-kg body, the body receives
   (a) an acceleration of 9.8 m/s^2 (b) a speed of 1 m/s
   (c) an acceleration of 980 m/s^2 (d) an acceleration of 1 m/s^2

6. A force of 20 N gives an object an acceleration of 5 m/s^2. What
   force will give the same object an acceleration of 16 m/s^2?
   (a) 64 N   (b) 32 N   (c) 4 N   (d) 256 N

31

7. A 10-kg mass is suspended by a rope. What is the acceleration if the tension in the rope is 118 N while the mass is in motion?
   (a) 4 m/s^2 (b) 2 m/s^2 (c) 11.8 m/s^2 (d) 20 m/s^2

8. A 64-1b body is suspended by a rope and accelerated upward with an acceleration of 8 ft/s^2. The tension in the rope is
   (a) 96 1b   (b) 16 1b   (c) 80 1b   (d) 48 1b

9. The mass m in Fig. 7-1 required to give the system an accelera-tion of 6 m/s^2 is approximately
   (a) 31.0 kg   (b) 31.6 kg   (c) 32.6 kg   (d) 41.9 kg

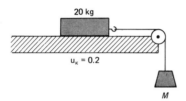

20 kg

u_k = 0.2

M

Fig. 7-1.

10. A 30-kg boy steps to shore from a 60-kg boat, giving the boat an acceleration of 2 m/s^2. If water resistance is neglected, the boy receives an acceleration of
    (a) -4 m/s^2 (b) -15 m/s^2 (c) -1 m/s^2 (d) -8 m/s^2

COMPLETION QUESTIONS

1. The acceleration an object receives is directly proportional to the _____ and inversely proportional to the _____.

2. The mass of a particle is equal to _____ divided by the _____.

3. In the Bgs, the mass unit, called a _____, is derived from the chosen unit of _____ for force.

4. In the mks system, the mass unit is the _____ and the derived unit is the _____.

5. Weight has the same units as the units of _____.

6. In the Bgs of units, the mass of an object is found by dividing its _____ by _____.

7. In the metric system, objects are usually described by giving their _____. In the Bgs, objects are described by giving their _____.

8. _____ is the force of gravitational attraction and is very much dependent on the _____.

9. If the force is held constant, an increase in _____ produces a proportionate _____ in acceleration.

10. If the unit of mass is the kilogram, the unit of force will be the _____ and the unit for acceleration will be _____.

ANSWERS TO TRUE-FALSE, MULTIPLE CHOICE, AND COMPLETION QUESTIONS

1. False	1. b	1. resultant force, mass
2. True	2. a	2. its weight, acceleration of
3. True	3. c	gravity
4. False	4. d	3. slug, pounds
5. False	5. d	4. kilogram, newton
6. True	6. a	5. force
7. True	7. b	6. weight, 32 ft/s^2
8. True	8. c	7. mass, weight
9. True	9. d	8. weight, acceleration of gravity
10. False	10. a	9. mass, decrease
		10. newton, m/s^2

CHAPTER 8. WORK, ENERGY, AND POWER

CONTENTS

OBJECTIVES

You should be able to:

1. State the conditions necessary for the performance of work.

2. Give two examples of an applied force which does no work and give one example of a displacement which occurs without the performance of work.

3. Write a mathematical formula for calculating the work accomplished by a given force and demonstrate that the formula is dimensionally correct.

4. Define the *foot-pound* and the *joule* as units of work or energy.

5. Illustrate your understanding of energy by giving two examples of each kind of energy discussed in this chapter.

6. Demonstrate by example or experiment the relationship between the performance of work and the corresponding change in kinetic energy.

7. Calculate the kinetic energy of an object when its mass or weight and its linear speed are given.

8. Write an equation which will determine the gravitational potential energy of a known mass or weight relative to a given location.

9. State verbally and mathematically your interpretation of the principle of conservation of mechanical energy, concluding with an example.

10. Apply your knowledge of initial and final energy states to the solution of physical problems.

11. Demonstrate by example or experiment your understanding of power and the procedure for its computation.

12. Define and compare the units of *kilowatt* and *horsepower* as they are used to measure power.

DEFINITIONS

Work - A scalar quantity equal to the product of the magnitude of the displacement and the component of the force in the direction of the displacement.

Energy - The ability to do work. When an object possesses energy, it is capable of exerting a force on another object in order to do work on it.

Potential energy - Energy possessed by a system by virtue of position or condition.

Kinetic energy - Energy possessed by a body by virtue of its motion.

Joule - A unit equivalent to the work done by a force of 1 N in moving an object through a distance of 1 m.

Foot-pound - A unit representing the work done by a force of 1 lb acting through a distance of 1 ft.

Conservation of energy - A principle which states that energy can never be created or destroyed but only changed in form.

Power - The time rate at which work is accomplished. Units of power are the watt, the foot-pound per second, and the horsepower.

Horsepower - A unit of power equivalent to 550 ft·lb/s, 33,000 ft·lb/min, or 746 W.

Watt - A unit of power representing work being accomplished at the rate of 1 J/s.

PHYSICAL CONCEPTS

1. The *work* done by a force **F** acting at an angle θ to the displacement s it causes is found from (see Fig. 8-1)

$$\text{Work} = (F \cos \theta)s$$

SI units: joule (J)   Bgs units: foot-pound (ft·lb)

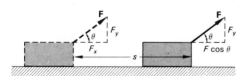

Fig. 8-1.

2. *Kinetic energy* E_K is the ability to do work as a result of motion. It has the same units as work and is found from

$$E_K = \tfrac{1}{2}mv^2 \qquad E_K = \tfrac{1}{2}\frac{W}{g}v^2$$

35

3. Gravitational *potential energy* is the energy which results from the position of an object relative to the earth. Potential energy E_p has the same units as work and is found from

$$E_p = Wh \qquad E_p = mgh$$

where W or mg is the weight of the object and h is the height above some reference position.

4. Work is equal to the change in kinetic energy.

$$Fs = \tfrac{1}{2}mv_f^2 - \tfrac{1}{2}mv_0^2$$

5. Conservation of mechanical energy under the action of a dissipative force F:

$$mgh = \tfrac{1}{2}mv_f^2 + Fs \qquad \text{initial } E_p = \text{final } E_k + \text{work}_F$$

6. *Power* is the rate at which work is done:

$$P = \frac{\text{work}}{t} \qquad P = \frac{Fs}{t} \qquad P = Fv$$

SI unit: watt (W)   Bgs unit: ft·lb/s

Other units: 1 kW = 10^3 W   1 hp = 550 ft·lb/s

TRUE-FALSE QUESTIONS

T   F   1.   In the absence of friction, air resistance, or other dissipative forces, the total kinetic energy remains constant.

T   F   2.   The total energy of a system of bodies in isolation may be defined as the sum of the individual kinetic and potential energies.

T   F   3.   All moving bodies possess kinetic energy.

T   F   4.   The work of a resultant force on a body is equal to the change in kinetic energy.

T   F   5.   As a body falls, its potential energy increases with its speed.

T   F   6.   A 1-hp engine will do work at a faster rate than a 1-kW engine.

T   F   7.   The kilowatthour is a unit of energy.

T   F   8.   As an object falls freely from the top of a building, its *total* energy remains constant.

T F 9. If we consider friction, the potential energy at the
          top of an inclined plane is less than it would be in the
          absence of friction.

T F 10. According to convention, negative work means that the
          direction of the work is downward or to the left.

MULTIPLE-CHOICE QUESTIONS

1. Which of the following is not necessary for work to be done?
   (a) an applied force
   (b) a force component along the displacement
   (c) a displacement
   (d) a constant speed

2. Which of the following is not a unit of work or energy?
   (a) N•m   (b) J   (c) ft•lb/s   (d) kW•h

3. The largest unit of power is the
   (a) kW   (b) W   (c) ft•lb/s   (d) horsepower

4. A force of 20 N moves a 10-kg block through a distance of 400 cm.
   The work done by the 20-N force is
   (a) 8000 J   (b) 80,000 J   (c) 80 J   (d) 80 N•m

5. A 10-kg block is lifted 20 m above the ground in a gravitational
   field. The work done by the field is
   (a) negative   (b) positive
   (c) equal to the final potential energy   (d) a vector quantity

6. In the above problem, the gravitational potential energy of the
   clock after it has been lifted 20 m is
   (a) 196 J   (b) 1960 J   (c) -1960 J   (d) 200 J

7. A 1-hp motor will lift a 200-lb block to what height in 2 s?
   (a) 0.01 ft   (b) 0.727 ft   (c) 100 ft   (d) 5.5 ft

8. A block of mass m slides down an inclined plane of height h and
   slope distance s. The kinetic energy at the bottom will be equal
   to
   (a) mgh (b) $\frac{1}{2}mv^2 - Fs$ (c) $mgh - Fs$ (d) $mgh + Fs$

9. A 2-kg ball has a potential energy of 6400 J at a point A above
   the ground. What will its velocity be when it strikes the ground
   after being released from point A?
   (a) 80 m/s   (b) 28.3 m/s   (c) 6400 m/s   (d) 800 m/s

10. A bullet whose initial kinetic energy is 400 J strikes a block
    where an 8000-N resistive force brings it to a stop. The depth
    of penetration into the wood is approximately
    (a) not enough information   (b) 0.2 m
    (c) 0.5 m   (d) 0.05 m

COMPLETION QUESTIONS

1. Three examples of potential energy are _____,
   _____, and _____.

2. The work of a resultant external force on a body is equal to the
   the change in _____ of the body.

3. The total mechanical energy of a body is the sum of its
   _____. This total is _____
   in the absence of friction.

4. A force of 1 N acting through a distance of 1 m represents
   _____ equal to 1 _____.

5. _____ is the rate at which work is done.

6. The net work done by a number of forces acting on the same object
   is equal to the work of the _____ force.

7. The kilowatthour is a unit of _____.

8. When the resultant force on an object is opposite to the direction
   of displacement, the work is considered _____.

9. Two things that are necessary in the performance of work are
   _____ and _____.

10 The product of force and velocity is a measure of _____.

ANSWERS TO TRUE-FALSE, MULTIPLE CHOICE, AND COMPLETION QUESTIONS

1.	False	1.	d	1.	a compressed spring, an elevated mass, a cocked rifle
2.	True	2.	c	2.	kinetic energy
3.	True	3.	a	3.	kinetic and potential energies, constant
4.	True	4.	c		
5.	False	5.	a	4.	work, J
6.	False	6.	b	5.	power
7.	True	7.	d	6.	resultant
8.	True	8.	c	7.	energy
9.	False	9.	a	8.	negative
10.	False	10.	d	9.	applied force, displacement
				10.	power

CHAPTER 9.   IMPULSE AND MOMENTUM

CONTENTS

OBJECTIVES

You should be able to:

1. Define *impulse* and *momentum* and suggest means for their measurement.

2. Write an equation illustrating the relationship of a *change in momentum* to the *impulse* and show that the relationship is dimensionally correct.

3. Demonstrate by example or experiment your understanding of the law of *conservation of momentum*.

4. Apply the law of conservation of momentum to problems involving colliding bodies.

5. Use your understanding of energy and momentum to explain what occurs after the balls are released in the following example: five metal balls are suspended by strings so that contact is made with each ball; two balls are pulled to one side and released.

6. Design an experiment which will measure the coefficient of restitution for a pair of surfaces.

7. Distinguish by definition and example between inelastic and elastic collisions.

8. Predict the velocities of two colliding bodies after impact when the coefficient of restitution, masses, and speeds before impact are given.

DEFINITIONS

Impulse - A vector quantity equal in magnitude to the product of a force and the time interval in which it acts ($F \, \Delta t$). The direction of an impulse is the same as the direction of the applied force.

Momentum - A vector quantity equal in magnitude to the product of a mass m and its velocity v. The direction is the same as that for the velocity.

Conservation of momentum - The total linear momentum of colliding
   bodies before impact is equal to their total momentum after
   impact. Thus, momentum is said to be conserved.

Elastic impact - A collision in which the total kinetic energy
   remains constant. No energy is lost because of heat or deformation.

Inelastic impact - A collision in which some of the initial energy
   possessed by the colliding objects is lost to heat or deformation.

Coefficient of restitution - The negative ratio of the relative
   velocity after collision to the relative velocity before collision. For elastic impacts the coefficient is equal to unit;
   for completely inelastic impacts it is zero.

PHYSICAL CONCEPTS

1. The *impulse* is the product of the average force F and the time
    interval Δt through which it acts.

     Impulse = $F \Delta t$ SI units: N·s   Bgs units: lb·s

2. The *momentum* of a particle is its mass times its velocity.

     Momentum $p = mv$ SI units: kg·m/s   Bgs units: slug·ft/s

3. The impulse is equal to the change in momentum:

     $\overline{F \Delta t \quad mv_f - mv_0}$ Note: N·s = kg·m/s (equivalent units)

4. *Conservation of momentum*: The total momentum before impact is
    equal to the total momentum after impact (see Fig. 9-1).

$$\overline{m_1 u_1 + m_2 u_2 = m_1 v_1 + m_2 v_2}$$

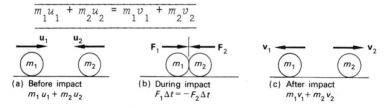

(a) Before impact
$m_1 u_1 + m_2 u_2$

(b) During impact
$F_1 \Delta t = -F_2 \Delta t$

(c) After impact
$m_1 v_1 + m_2 v_2$

Fig. 9-1. Head-on collision of two masses.

5. The *coefficient of restitution* is found from relative velocities
    before and after collision or from the rebound height:

$$e = \frac{v_2 - v_1}{u_1 - u_2} \qquad e = \sqrt{\frac{h_2}{h_1}}$$

6. For a completely elastic collision, $e = 1$.
   For a completely inelastic collision, $e = 0$.

TRUE-FALSE QUESTIONS

T F 1. The total linear energy of colliding bodies before impact must always equal the total energy after impact.

T F 2. The vigor with which a body restores itself to its original shape after deformation is a measure of its elasticity or restitution.

T F 3. A coefficient of restitution equal to 0.5 is an indication that the collision is inelastic.

T F 4. The units for impulse are equivalent to the units for momentum.

T F 5. An object that has linear momentum also has kinetic energy.

T F 6. The foot-pound per second is a unit of linear momentum.

T F 7. An object bouncing against a floor with perfectly elastic collisions will continue to bounce at the same height.

T F 8. Momentum is a scalar quantity.

T F 9. Momentum is conserved in all collisions.

T F 10. The kilogram-meter per second is a larger unit of momentum than the slug-foot per second.

MULTIPLE-CHOICE QUESTIONS

1. Which of the following is *not* a unit of impulse?
   (a) lb·s   (b) N·s   (c) lb·h   (d) N·m

2. When the velocity of a body is doubled,
   (a) its kinetic energy is doubled
   (b) its momentum is doubled
   (c) its acceleration is doubled
   (d) its potential energy is doubled

3. A 100-kg astronaut releases 1 g of gas from a special pistol at a speed of 50 m/s. As a result, he moves in the opposite direction at
   (a) 5 cm/s   (b) 50 cm/s   (c) 0.5 cm/s   (d) 0.05 cm/s

4. If a car is to gain momentum, it must
   (a) move rapidly   (b) accelerate
   (c) lose inertia   (d) lose weight

5. The face of a golf club exerts an average force of 4000 N while it is in contact with the golf ball. If the impulse is 80 N·s, the time of contact is
   (a) 0.2 s   (b) 0.02 s   (c) 2 s   (d) 0.002 s

6. In a completely elastic collision, which of the following quantities need *not* be conserved?
   (a) kinetic energy   (b) momentum
   (c) mass   (d) potential energy

7. Eight steel balls are suspended from equal heights by threads so that they are all in contact. If two balls are pulled away to the left and released,
   (a) one ball will leave from the right with twice the speed
   (b) two balls will leave from the right at approximately the same speed
   (c) either (a) or (b) might apply
   (d) neither (a) nor (b) applies

8. A 40-kg cart moving at 3 m/s makes a head-on collision with a 20-kg cart at rest, as illustrated in Fig. 9-2. If the collision is completely inelastic, the speed with which the carts leave the impact is approximately
   (a) 2 m/s   (b) 6 m/s   (c) 20 m/s   (d) 0.2 m/s

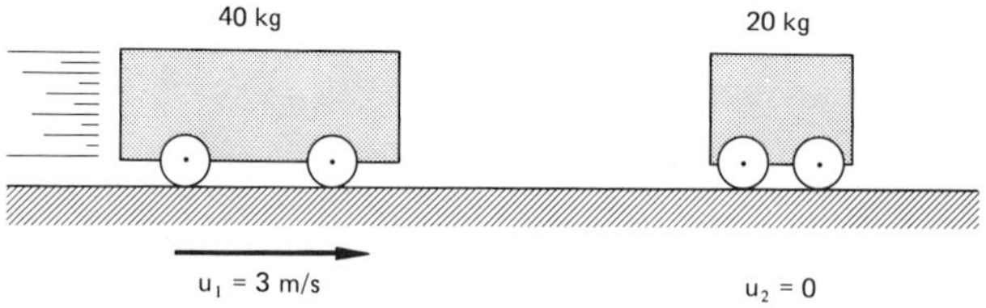

Fig. 9-2.

9. If the collision in Problem 8 is completely elastic, the speed of the 20-kg cart after collision will be approximately
   (a) 6 m/s   (b) 3 m/s   (c) 4 m/s   (d) 2 m/s

10. A 10-g bullet is fired into a 2-kg block of wood suspended from a cord. If the block and bullet rise to a height of 10 cm after impact, the initial velocity of the bullet was approximately
    (a) 2.8 m/s   (b) 281 m/s   (c) 235 m/s   (d) 28.1 m/s

COMPLETION QUESTIONS

1. An elastic collision is one in which both _____ and _____ are conserved.

2. _____ is the product of mass and velocity and has the metric units _____.

3. The negative ratio of the relative velocities after impact to the relative velocities before impact is known as the _____.

4. The product of the average force acting on a body and the time of action is called the _____, and it is equal to the _____ of the body.

5. The coefficient of restitution has a maximum value of _____ for a perfectly _____ impact and a minimum value of _____ for a perfectly _____ impact.

6. If two colliding bodies stick together after impact and move off with the same velocity, the impact is said to be _____.

7. In the Bgs, the unit for impulse is _____, and the unit for momentum is _____.

8. When a rifle is fired, the _____ of the bullet is the same as the recoil _____ of the rifle.

9. The square root of the ratio of the height to which a ball bounces to its height originally is a measure of the _____.

10. The vigor with which an object restores itself to its original shape after deformation is a measure of its _____.

ANSWERS TO TRUE-FALSE, MULTIPLE CHOICE, AND COMPLETION QUESTIONS

1.	False	1.	d	1. momentum, kinetic energy
2.	True	2.	b	2. momentum, kilogram-meters per second
3.	True	3.	d	3. coefficient of restitution
4.	True	4.	b	4. impulse, change in momentum
5.	True	5.	b	5. 1, elastic, 0, inelastic
6.	False	6.	d	6. completely inelastic
7.	True	7.	b	7. pounds per second, slug-feet per second
8.	False	8.	a	8. momentum, momentum
9.	True	9.	c	9. coefficient of restitution
10.	False	10.	b	10. elasticity

CHAPTER 10.   UNIFORM CIRCULAR MOTION

CONTENTS

OBJECTIVES

You should be able to:

1. State the conditions necessary for uniform circular motion and give two examples.

2. Explain how acceleration is possible without a change in speed.

3. Calculate the centripetal acceleration when the linear speed of an object rotating in a circle of known radius is given.

4. Demonstrate that all boxed equations in this chapter are dimensionally correct.

5. Define the *period* and *frequency* of rotation and relate them to the linear speed of an object moving along a circular path.

6. Demonstrate by example or experiment your understanding of centripetal force and its relationship to the linear speed of a mass moving in a circular path.

7. Give at least two examples illustrating your understanding of the distinction between the terms *centripetal force* and *centrifugal force*.

8. Apply your knowledge of centripetal force to the solution of problems similar to those illustrated in the text for banking of curves, the conical pendulum, and motion in a vertical circle.

9. Describe at least two practical applications of centripetal force.

10. Write verbal and mathematical statements of Newton's univeral law of gravitation.

11. Describe an experiment which would measure the universal gravitation constant.

DEFINITIONS

Uniform circular motion - Circular motion in which the speed is constant and only the direction changes.

Centripetal acceleration - The acceleration toward the center to which any particle moving in a circular orbit is subject. The change in velocity per unit of time may consist only of directional changes. The magnitude is equal to v^2/R, where v is the orbital velocity and R is the radius.

Centripetal force - The inward force necessary to impart centripetal acceleration and therefore maintain circular motion. Its magnitude is equal to the product of mass and centripetal acceleration.

Universal law of gravitation - Each particle in the universe attracts each other particle with a force that is directly proportional to the product of their masses and inversely proportional to the square of the distance between them.

Linear speed - Distance covered per unit of time whether the distance is along a straight line or along a curved path.

Period - In circular motion, the time for one complete revolution.

Frequency - In circular motion, the number of complete revolutions occurring per unit of time. Units are revolutions per minute and revolutions per second.

Critical speed - For motion in a vertical circle, the minimum speed at the bottom of the path for which the motion will remain circular.

Conical pendulum - A mass m revolving in a horizontal circle with constant speed v at the end of a cord of length L.

PHYSICAL CONCEPTS

1. The linear speed v of an object in uniform circular motion can be calculated from the period T or frequency f:

$$v = \frac{2\pi R}{T} \qquad v = 2\pi f R$$

2. The centripetal acceleration a_c is found from the linear speed, the period, or the frequency as follows:

$$a_c = \frac{v^2}{R} \qquad a_c = \frac{4\pi^2 R}{T^2} \qquad a_c = 4\pi^2 f^2 R$$

3. The centripetal force F_c is equal to the product of the mass m and the centripetal acceleration a_c. It is given by

$$F_c = \frac{mv^2}{R} \qquad F_c = 4\pi^2 f^2 mR$$

45

4. Other useful formulas are as follows:

$$v = \sqrt{\mu_s gR}$$ maximum speed without slipping

$$\tan \theta = \frac{v^2}{gR}$$ banking angle or conical pendulum

$$f = \frac{1}{2\pi} \sqrt{\frac{g}{h}}$$ frequency of a conical pendulum

TRUE-FALSE QUESTIONS

T   F   1. When a rock is made to move in a circular path at the end of a string, an outward force is exerted on the rock.

T   F   2. If the string breaks in Question 1, centripetal acceleration will cause the rock to move inward.

T   F   3. Centripetal and centrifugal forces have the same magnitudes but are opposite in directions; they don't cancel because they act on different objects.

T   F   4. When a car moves in a horizontal circle on a level road, the centripetal force is exerted by the tires.

T   F   5. The maximum speed with which a car can negotiate a curve does not depend on the weight of the car.

T   F   6. The period of revolution may be thought of as the number of complete revolutions per second.

T   F   7. Just as a resultant force is needed to change the speed of a body, a resultant force is necessary to change its direction.

T   F   8. Uniform circular motion is motion in which the linear speed changes at a constant rate.

T   F   9. The formula for computing the banking angle will also apply for the angle that the cord makes with the vertical for a conical pendulum.

T   F   10. If two masses are separated by twice the distance, they will experience one-half the gravitational attraction.

MULTIPLE-CHOICE QUESTIONS

1. A ball is tied to a string and swung in a horizontal circle. When the string breaks, the ball will follow a path that is
(a) toward the center   (b) away from the center
(c) at a tangent to its circular path   (d) none of these

2. The force exerted on the ball above is a
   (a) centrifugal force   (b) centripetal force
   (c) gravitational force   (d) fictitious force

3. A body traveling in a circular path at constant speed
   (a) has an outward acceleration   (b) has inward acceleration
   (c) has constant velocity   (d) is not accelerated

4. An object makes one complete revolution in 0.5 s. Its frequency
   is
   (a) 2 s   (b) 5 rev/s   (c) 2 rev/s   (d) 0.5 rev/s

5. An object swings at the end of a string in uniform circular
   motion. Which of the following changes would not cause an
   increased centripetal force?
   (a) a longer string   (b) a shorter string
   (c) a greater linear speed   (d) a larger mass

6. The linear speed of an object swinging in a circular path of
   radius 2 m with a frequency of 5 rev/s is
   (a) 2π m/s   (b) 20π m/s   (c) 4π m/s   (d) 10π m/s

7. The centripetal acceleration of a 2-kg mass swinging in a 0.4-m
   radius with a linear speed of 4 m/s has a centripetal acceleration of
   (a) 4 m/s^2 (b) 40 m/s^2 (c) 10 m/s^2 (d) 20 m/s^2

8. An 8-kg ball is swung in a horizontal circle by a cord of length
   2 m. If the period is 0.5 s, the tension in the cord is
   approximately
   (a) 264 N   (b) 202 N   (c) 1200 N   (d) 2527 N

9. The banking angle for a curve of radius 400 ft for speed of
   60 mi/h should be approximately
   (a) 31°   (b) 16°   (c) 26°   (d) 37°

10. The gravitational constant is 6.67 x 10^{-11} N·m^2/kg^2. What is the
    gravitational force between two 4-kg balls separated by 0.2 m?
    (a) 5.34 x 10^{-7} N   (b) 2.67 x 10^{-8} N
    (c) 1.33 x 10^{-8} N   (d) 6.67 x 10^{-8} N

COMPLETION QUESTIONS

1. Uniform circular motion is motion in which there is no change in
   _____ but only a change in _____.

2. The _____ is the number of revolutions per unit
   of time, whereas the _____ is the time for one
   revolution.

3. For a body moving in a horizontal circle, doubling the linear
   speed has the effect of increasing the centripetal acceleration
   by a factor of _____.

4. The gravitational force between two particles is directly proportional to the product of their _____ and inversely
proportional to the _____ of the _____
between them.

5. The force required to keep mass moving in a circular path at constant speed v is called the _____ force and has a
magnitude equal to _____, where R is the radius of
the circle.

6. The proper banking angle θ to eliminate the necessity for a
frictional force is given by the relation _____
where v is the velocity, R is the radius of the curve, and g is
the acceleration due to gravity.

7. Whenever the centripetal force acts on an object, there is an
equal and opposite _____ force exerted by the
object.

8. When a curve is not banked, the centripetal force is provided by
_____.

9. The _____ speed is the minimum speed to maintain
circular motion in a vertical plane.

10. The correct set of Bgs units for the gravitational constant is
_____.

ANSWERS TO TRUE-FALSE, MULTIPLE CHOICE, AND COMPLETION QUESTIONS

1. False	1. c	1. speed, direction
2. False	2. b	2. frequency, period
3. True	3. b	3. 4
4. False	4. c	4. masses, square, distance
5. True	5. a	5. centripetal, mv^2/R
6. False	6. b	6. $\tan \theta = v^2/gR$
7. True	7. b	7. centrifugal
8. False	8. d	8. friction
9. True	9. a	9. critical
10. False	10. b	10. $lb \cdot ft^2/slug^2$

CHAPTER 11. ROTATION OF RIGID BODIES

CONTENTS

1. Angular Displacement
2. Angular Velocity
3. Angular Acceleration
4. Relation between Angular and Linear Motion
5. Rotational Kinetic Energy: Moment of Inertia
6. The Second Law of Motion in Rotation
7. Rotational Work and Power
8. Angular Momentum
9. Conservation of Angular Momentum

OBJECTIVES

You should be able to:

1. Define and illustrate the *degree*, the *revolution*, and the *radian* as angular measures and be able to convert from one unit to the other.

2. Write the relationship between angular displacement and circum-linear displacement and use this knowledge problems.

3. Define *angular velocity* and describe a procedure for its measurement.

4. Define *angular acceleration* and suggest an experiment for its measurement.

5. Compute the angular speed of a rotating object in radians per second when the frequency of rotation is given.

6. Draw analogies relating angular-motion parameters (θ, ω, α) to linear-motion parameters (s, v, a) and solve problems involving angular acceleration in a manner similar to that learned earlier for problems involving linear acceleration (refer to Table 11-1 in the text).

7. Write and apply the mathematical relationships between linear speed or acceleration and angular speed or acceleration.

8. Define the *moment of inertia* of a body and describe how this quantity and the angular speed of an object determine the *rotational* kinetic energy.

9. State verbally and mathematically Newton's second law of motion as it relates to rotational acceleration.

10. Define *rotational work* and *rotational power* and give formulas for their computation.

11. Define *angular momentum* and give at least two examples illustrating your understanding of how it is conserved.

12. Demonstrate that all boxed equations appearing in this chapter are dimensionally consistent.

DEFINITIONS

Angular displacement - The amount of rotation a body describes, denoted by an angle measured in degrees, radians, or revolutions.

Angular velocity - The time rate of change of the angular displacement; it is usually expressed in radians per second.

Angular acceleration - The time rate of change in angular velocity, normally expressed in radians per second per second (rad/s^2).

Moment of inertia - For rotational motion, the moment of inertia I of a body about a particular axis is the rotational analog of mass in linear motion. It depends on how the mass of a body is distributed about the rotational axis.

Rotational kinetic energy - Energy possessed by a body by virtue of its moment of inertia I and its rotational speed ω.

Radius of gyration - The radial distance from the center of rotation of a rigid body to a point at which the total mass of the body might be concentrated without changing its moment of inertia.

Rotational work - The scalar product of rotational torque and the angular displacement it causes.

Rotational power - The rate at which rotational work is accomplished; it is equal to the product of torque and angular speed.

Angular momentum - With reference to a fixed axis of rotation, the angular momentum is equal to the product of a body's angular velocity and its moment of inertia.

PHYSICAL CONCEPTS

1. The angle in radians is the ratio of the arc distance s to the radius R of the arc. Symbolically we write:

$$\theta = \frac{s}{R} \qquad s = \theta R$$

    The radian is a unitless ratio of two lengths.

2. Angular velocity, which is the rate of angular displacement, can be calculated from θ or from the frequency or rotation:

$$\bar{\omega} = \frac{\theta}{t} \qquad \bar{\omega} = 2\pi f \qquad \text{Average angular velocity}$$

3. Angular acceleration is the time rate of change in angular speed:

$$\alpha = \frac{\omega_f - \omega_0}{t} \qquad \text{Angular acceleration}$$

4. By comparing θ to s, ω to v, and α to a, the following equations can be utilized for angular acceleration problems:

$$\theta = \frac{\omega_f - \omega_0}{2} t$$

$$\omega_f = \omega_0 + \alpha t$$

$$\theta = \omega_0 t + \tfrac{1}{2}\alpha t^2$$

$$2\alpha\theta = \omega_f^2 - \omega_0^2$$

When any three of the five parameters $\theta, \alpha, t, \omega_f$, and ω_0 are given, the other two can be found from one of these equations. Choose a direction of rotation as being positive throughout your calculations.

5. The following equations are useful when comparing linear motion with rotational motion:

$$v = \omega R \qquad a_T = \alpha R$$

6. Other useful relationships:

$$I = \Sigma m R^2 \qquad \text{moment of inertia}$$

$$I = m\kappa^2 \qquad \text{radius of gyration}$$

$$\text{work} = L\theta \qquad \text{work}$$

$$H = I\omega \qquad \text{angular momentum}$$

$$E_\kappa = \tfrac{1}{2}\omega I^2 \qquad \text{rotational kinetic energy}$$

$$L = I\alpha \qquad \text{Newton's law}$$

$$P = L\omega \qquad \text{power}$$

$$I\omega_f = I\omega_0 \qquad \text{conservation of angular momentum}$$

TRUE-FALSE QUESTIONS

T   F   1.   If the sum of the external torques acting on a body or system of bodies is zero, the angular momentum is also zero.

T   F   2.   An angle of 1 rad is an angle whose arc distance s is equal in length to the radius R.

T F 3. Angular frequency and angular velocity are representations of the same physical quantity.

T F 4. Both angular acceleration and tangential acceleration represent a rate of change in angular speed.

T F 5. The rotational kinetic energy of an object on a rotating platform decreases as the object moves toward the center of rotation.

T F 6. A solid disk of mass M will roll to the bottom of an incline quicker than a circular hoop of the same mass and diameter.

T F 7. Torque is the rotational analog of linear force.

T F 8. A resultant torque will produce an angular acceleration directly proportional to the applied torque and inversely proportional to the total mass of the object.

T F 9. The angular impulse is equal to a change in rotational kinetic energy.

T F 10. For a rotating rigid body, the ratio of linear speed to angular speed is equal to the radius of revolution.

MULTIPLE-CHOICE QUESTIONS

1. Increasing the angular speed of a rotating body will not cause an increase in
   (a) rotational kinetic energy   (b) angular momentum
   (c) the moment of inertia   (d) linear speed

2. Which of the following would not necessarily cause angular acceleration?
   (a) change in frequency   (b) change in angular displacement
   (c) change in angular speed   (d) change in linear speed

3. A point on the edge of a rotating disk of radius 8 m moves through an angle of 2 rad. The length of the arc described by the point is
   (a) 4 m   (b) 0.25 m   (c) 16 m   (d) 4π rad

4. If the frequency is 2 rev/s, the angular speed is
   (a) 4π rad/s   (b) 2π rad/s   (c) π rad/s   (d) 4 rad/s

5. A flywheel increases its angular speed from 4 to 12 rad/s in 4 s. Its angular acceleration is
   (a) 3 rad/s^2 (b) 12 rad/s^2 (c) 4 rad/s^2 (d) 2 rad/s^2

6. A drive shaft has a frequency of rotation of 1200 rpm. The linear speed of flyweights positioned 2 ft from the axis is approximately
   (a) 80π ft/s   (b) 40π ft/s   (c) 40 ft/s   (d) 20 ft/s

7. A circular disk has a moment of inertia of 2 kg·m^2 and a rotational kinetic energy of 400 J. The angular speed must be approximately
   (a) 200 rad/s   (b) 40 rad/s   (c) 400 rad/s   (d) 20 rad/s

8. Which of the following objects has the largest moment of inertia assuming they all have the same mass and the same radius?
   (a) a solid sphere   (b) a solid disk
   (b) a circular hoop   (d) a solid cylinder

9. A circular grinding disk of radius 0.5 ft has a moment of inertia of 16 slug·ft^2 and is rotating at 600 rpm. The frictional force applied to the edge of the disk, in order to stop the wheel in 10 s, is approximately
   (a) 201 lb   (b) 100 lb   (c) 402 lb   (d) 32 lb

10. A wheel with angular moment of 10 kg·m^2/s has a moment of inertia equal to 0.5 kg·m^2. Its angular speed is
    (a) 40 rad/s   (b) 20 rad/s   (c) 5 rad/s   (d) 0.05 rad/s

COMPLETION QUESTIONS

1. The angular displacement in _____ is the ratio of the length of arc to its _____.

2. If the sum of the external _____ acting on a body or system of bodies is zero, the angular _____ remains unchanged. This is a statement of the conservation of _____.

3. Rotation work is the scalar product of _____ and _____.

4. A resultant torque applied to a rigid body will always result in an _____ that is directly proportional to the applied _____ and inversely proportional to the body's _____.

5. The Bgs units of the moment of inertia are _____.

6. The ratio of the tangential acceleration to the _____ is equal to the radius of revolution.

7. In rotational motion, the final angular velocity is equal to the initial _____ plus the product of the angular _____ and _____.

8. The _____ is the radial distance from the center of rotation to a point at which the total mass of the body might be concentrated without changing its _____ _____.

9. The linear speed divided by the radius of rotation is the
_____ of the body.

10. Rotational power is equal to the product of _____ and
angular _____.

ANSWERS TO TRUE-FALSE, MULTIPLE CHOICE, AND COMPLETION QUESTIONS

1. False	1. c	1. radians, radius
2. True	2. b	2. torques, momentum, angular
3. True	3. c	momentum
4. False	4. a	3. torque, angular displacement
5. True	5. d	4. angular acceleration, torque,
6. False	6. a	moment of inertia
7. True	7. d	5. slug·ft^2
8. False	8. c	6. angular acceleration
9. False	9. a	7. angular velocity, acceleration,
10. True	10. b	time
		8. radius of gyration, moment of
		inertia
		9. angular velocity
		10. torque, velocity

CHAPTER 12.   SIMPLE MACHINES

CONTENTS

OBJECTIVES

You should be able to:

1. Describe a simple machine and its operation in *general terms* to the extent that *efficiency* and *conservation of energy* are explained.

2. Write and use formulas for computing the efficiency of a simple machine in terms of *work* and *power*.

3. Distinguish by definition and example between *ideal* mechanical advantage and *actual* mechanical advantage.

4. Name at least four examples of the application of the principle of the *lever*.

5. Give four examples of the application of the principle of the *inclined plane*.

6. Draw a diagram of each of the following simple machines and beside each diagram write a formula for computing the ideal mechanical advantage:
   (a) lever   (b) inclined plane (c) wheel and axle (d) wedge
   (e) screw jack   (f) gears   (g) pulley systems (h) belt drive

7. Compute, in physical problems involving known parameters, the mechanical advantage and the efficiency of the simple machines listed under Objective 6.

DEFINITIONS

Machine - Any device which transmits the application of a force into useful work.

Efficiency - The ratio of the work output by a machine to the work input, usually expressed as a percentage.

Lever - A simple machine consisting of any rigid bar pivoted at a certain point called the fulcrum. The principle of the lever is used in many simple machines, such as pulley systems and gears.

55

Inclined plane - A simple machine which uses a gradual slope to give the desired mechanical advantage (the wedge and the screw).

Actual mechanical advantage - The ratio of an output force to the input force under actual conditions, i.e., considering friction.

Ideal mechanical advantage - The ratio of the distance the input force moves to the distance the output force moves under ideal conditions, i.e., in the absence of friction.

Pitch - The distance between two adjacent threads on a screw.

Speed ratio - In pulleys or gears, the ratio of the angular velocity of the input pulley or gear to the angular velocity of the output pulley or gear.

PHYSICAL CONCEPTS

1. A simple machine is a device which converts a single input force F_i into a single output force F_o. The input force moves through a distance s_i and the output force moves a distance s_o. There are two mechanical advantages:

$$M_A = \frac{F_o}{F_i} \qquad \text{actual mechanical advantage (friction considered)}$$

$$M_I = \frac{s_o}{s_i} \qquad \text{ideal mechanical advantage (assumes no friction)}$$

2. The efficiency of a machine is a ratio of output work to input work. It is normally expressed as a percentage and can be calculated from any of the following relations:

$$E = \frac{\text{work output}}{\text{work input}} \qquad E = \frac{\text{power output}}{\text{power input}} \qquad E = \frac{M_A}{M_I}$$

3. The ideal mechanical advantages for a number of simple machines are given below.

$$M_I = \frac{F_o}{F_i} = \frac{r_i}{r_o} \qquad \text{lever}$$

$$M_I = \frac{F_o}{F_i} = \frac{R}{r} \qquad \text{wheel and axle}$$

$$M_I = \frac{D_o}{D_i} = \frac{\omega_i}{\omega_o} \qquad \text{belt drive}$$

$$M_I = \frac{W}{F_i} = \frac{s}{h}$$

inclined plane

$$M_I = \frac{L}{t}$$

wedge

$$M_I = \frac{N_o}{N_i} = \frac{D_o}{D_i}$$

gears

$$M_I = \frac{s_i}{s_o} = \frac{2\pi R}{p}$$

screw jack

TRUE-FALSE QUESTIONS

T F 1. The efficiency of a machine is defined as the ratio of the work input to the work output.

T F 2. The actual mechanical advantage of a machine can never be less than unity.

T F 3. The wheel and axle is an application of the principle of the lever.

T F 4. A single fixed pulley offers no mechanical advantage; it only serves to change the direction of an input force.

T F 5. In a pulley system with a speed ratio greater than 1, the output torque is less than the input torque.

T F 6. In a machine using two gears in which the number of teeth on the input gear is greater than the number of teeth on the output gear, there will be a reduction in the output torque.

T F 7. The speed ratio ω_i/ω_o represents the ideal mechanical advantage and not the actual mechanical advantage.

T F 8. In a belt drive, maximum efficiency is obtained for minimum belt tension.

T F 9. For an inclined plane, the actual mechanical advantage is the ratio of the slope distance to the height of the plane.

T F 10. For a screw jack, a larger pitch results in a smaller mechanical advantage.

MULTIPLE-CHOICE QUESTIONS

1. Which of the following ratios does *not* represent the mechanical advantage of a machine?
   (a) D_o/D_i (b) ω_o/ω_i (c) N_o/N_i (d) F_o/F_i

2. Which of the following is *not* an indication of the efficiency of a machine?
   (a) M_A/M_I (b) P_o/P_i (c) $F_o r_o/F_i r_i$ (d) $L_o\omega_o/L_i\omega_i$

3. The actual mechanical advantage may be increased for a given machine by
   (a) increasing F_i (b) increasing F_O
   (c) lubrication   (d) none of these

4. Which of the following machines is *not* an application of the lever principle?
   (a) screw jack   (b) wheelbarrow
   (c) wheel and axle   (d) pliers

5. An 80-hp motor has an efficiency of 60 percent. The output power is approximately
   (a) 133 hp   (b) 75 hp   (c) 60 hp   (d) 48 hp

6. An iron pipe 10 ft long is used to lift a 400-lb weight. If the fulcrum is placed 2 ft from the weight, the force which must be exerted at the end of the pipe is approximately
   (a) 200 lb   (b) 100 lb   (c) 40 lb   (d) 80 lb

7. The ideal mechanical advantage of a belt drive is 4.0. If the angular speed of the input pulley is 8 rad/s, the angular speed of the output pulley is
   (a) 2 rad/s   (b) 32 rad/s   (c) 0.5 rad/s   (d) 4 rad/s

8. A 100-lb box is pushed up a 200-ft ramp to a height of 20 ft. The ideal mechanical advantage is approximately
   (a) 4   (b) 10   (c) 5   (d) 0.1

9. Consider a belt drive in which the diameter of the driving pulley is 8 cm and the diameter of the driven pulley is 24 cm. If the efficiency is 50 percent, what is the actual mechanical advantage?
   (a) 15   (b) 6   (c) 1.5   (d) 3

10. In the operation of a screw jack of pitch 0.1 in., the input force of 4 lb turns through a circle of radius 2 ft, lifting an 80-lb weight. The efficiency is approximately
    (a) 48 percent   (b) 14.4 percent
    (c) 20 percent   (d) 1.3 percent

COMPLETION QUESTIONS

1. The efficiency of a machine is defined as the ratio of the _____ to the _____.

2. In general, for a simple machine the _____ _____ is defined as the ratio of the output force to the input force. The _____ _____ is the ratio of the distance the _____ force moves to the distance the _____ force moves.

3. Three applications of the lever principle are demonstrated by the following tools: _____, _____, and _____.

4. If the speed ratio is greater than 1, the machine produces an output torque _____ than the input torque.

5. Three common types of gears are _____ gears, _____ gears, and _____ gears.

6. The ideal mechanical advantage of a wedge is equal to its _____ plus the _____.

7. For a simple machine, the work input is equal to the _____ _____ plus the _____.

8. The ideal mechanical advantage of a set of gears is equal to the ratio of the _____ on the output gear to the _____ on the input gear.

9. For a screw jack, the reciprocal of the number of threads per inch is the _____ of the screw.

10. In a single movable pulley, the input force moves through _____ the distance that the output force moves, resulting in a mechanical advantage of _____.

ANSWERS TO TRUE-FALSE, MULTIPLE CHOICE, AND COMPLETION QUESTIONS

1.	False	1.	b	1.	work output, work input
2.	False	2.	c	2.	actual mechanical advantage, ideal mechanical advantage, input, output
3.	True	3.	c		
4.	True	4.	a		
5.	False	5.	d	3.	nutcracker, wheelbarrow, crowbar
6.	True	6.	b		
7.	True	7.	a	4.	greater
8.	True	8.	b	5.	planetary, bevel, helical
9.	False	9.	c	6.	length, thickness
10.	True	10.	d	7.	work against friction, work output
				8.	number of teeth, number of teeth
				9.	pitch
				10.	twice, 2

CHAPTER 13. ELASTICITY

CONTENTS

OBJECTIVES

You should be able to:

1. Distinguish between elastic and inelastic bodies and give two examples of each.

2. Determine the spring constant when a spring and a set of known weights are given.

3. Define *stress* and give examples of *tensile*, *compressive*, and *shear* stresses.

4. Give at least two illustrations of your understanding of *strain*.

5. Distinguish between the terms *elastic limit* and *ultimate strength* as they relate to an elastic body.

6. Write a general statement of *Hooke's law* as it applies to elastic bodies.

7. Write formulas for predicting *Young's modulus*, *bulk modulus*, and *shear modulus* and beside each formula construct a sketch illustrating your understanding of each concept, complete with labels to define formula parameters.

8. Apply the relations listed in Objective 7 to the solution of physical problems similar to examples given in the text.

9. Give an example which illustrates your understanding of the term *compressibility*.

DEFINITIONS

<u>Elasticity</u> - The property whereby a body, when deformed, automatically recovers its normal configuration when the deforming forces are removed.

<u>Hooke's law</u> - Provided that the elastic limit is not exceeded, an elastic deformation (strain) is directly proportional to the magnitude of the applied force per unit area (stress).

<u>Spring constant</u> - A property of a material which is equal to the ratio of an applied force to the change in dimension it causes.

60

Stress - The ratio of an applied force to the area over which it acts.

Strain - The relative change in the dimensions or shape of a body as a result of an applied stress.

Elastic limit - The maximum stress a body can experience without becoming permanently deformed.

Ultimate strength - The greatest stress a material can withstand without rupturing.

Young's modulus - The modulus of elasticity which relates to the change in a single dimension caused by a parallel stress. For a rod or wire, it is the ratio of force per unit area to the resultant change in length per unit length.

Shear modulus - The property of a material defined as the ratio of an applied stress to the resulting angle of shear expressed in radians.

Bulk modulus - The negative ratio of an applied force per unit area to the resultant change in volume per unit volume.

Compressibility - The fractional change in volume per unit increase in pressure. It is the reciprocal of the bulk modulus.

PHYSICAL CONCEPTS

1. According to *Hooke's law,* an elastic body will deform or elongate an amount s under the application of a force F. The constant of proportionality k is the *spring constant:*

$$F = ks \qquad k = \frac{F}{s} \qquad \text{Hooke's law}$$

2. *Stress* is the ratio of an applied force to the area over which it acts. *Strain* is the relative change in dimensions which results from the stress. For example,

$$\text{Longitudinal stress} = \frac{F}{A} \qquad \text{longitudinal strain} = \frac{\Delta l}{l}$$

3. The *modulus of elasticity* is the constant ratio of stress to strain:

$$\text{Modulus of elasticity} = \frac{stress}{strain}$$

4. *Young's modulus* Y is for longitudinal deformations:

$$Y = \frac{F/A}{\Delta l/l} \qquad \text{or} \qquad Y = \frac{Fl}{A \cdot \Delta l} \qquad \text{Young's modulus}$$

61

5. A shearing strain occurs when an angular deformation ϕ is produced:

$$S = \frac{F/A}{\tan \phi} \quad \text{or} \quad S = \frac{F/A}{d/l} \quad \text{shear modulus}$$

The meaning of these symbols is evident from Fig. 13-1.

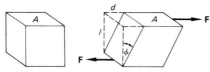

Fig. 13-1.   Shear modulus.

6. Whenever an applied stress results in a change in volume ΔV, you will need the *bulk modulus B*, given by

$$B = - \frac{F/A}{\Delta V/V} \quad \text{bulk modulus}$$

The reciprocal of the bulk modulus is called the compressibility.

TRUE-FALSE QUESTIONS

T F 1. A material having a large spring constant will experience a greater change in length for a given applied force than a material with a small spring constant.

T F 2. Stress is the relative change in the dimensions or shape of a body as the result of an applied force.

T F 3. The ultimate strength of a material is the greatest stress it can withstand without rupturing.

T F 4. The smaller the bulk modulus of a material, the higher its compressibility.

T F 5. The radian may be a unit of strain.

T F 6. The modulus of elasticity has the same units as stress.

T F 7. Young's modulus is constant for a particular material but varies with the length and cross-sectional area of a wire.

T F 8. Water has a greater compressibility than steel.

T F 9. Usually the shearing strain can be approximated by the tangent of the shearing angle.

T F 10. Young's modulus applies for compressive stresses as well as for tensile stresses.

MULTIPLE-CHOICE QUESTIONS

1. Two wires, A and B, are made of the same material and are sub-
   jected to the same loads. The strain is greater for A when
   (a) A is twice as long as B
   (b) A has twice the diameter of B
   (c) A has twice the length and half the diameter
   (d) A has twice the diameter and half the length

2. A shearing stress acting on a body changes its
   (a) shape   (b) volume   (c) length   (d) area

3. A unit for strain is the
   (a) inch   (b) pound per square inch
   (b) newton per centimeter   (d) radian

4. The volume strain for a constant applied force increases directly
   with an increase in
   (a) surface area   (b) compressibility
   (c) volume   (d) bulk modulus

5. According to Hooke's law, an applied force will result in an
   elongation equal to
   (a) ks (b) s/k (c) F/s (d) F/k

6. The modulus of rigidity is another name for
   (a) compressibility   (b) bulk modulus
   (c) shear modulus   (d) Young's modulus

7. When a force of 20 N produces an elongation of 0.4 cm, the
   spring constant is
   (a) 5 N/cm   (b) 50 N/cm   (c) 8 N·cm   (d) 0.02 cm/N

8. The cross-sectional area of a 20-in copper wire is 0.001 in.^{2}. A
   force of 400 lb causes a stress of
   (a) 4×10^5 lb/in.^{2} (b) 0.4 lb/in.^{2}
   (c) 20 lb/in.   (d) 50 lb/in.

9. In Question 8 the Young's modulus for copper is 17×10^6 lb/in.^{2}.
   The resultant elongation of the wire is approximately
   (a) 0.012 in.   (b) 0.12 in.   (c) 0.47 in.   (d) 0.0047 in.

10. A mechanical press contains 2 m^3 of oil (B = 1700 MPa). If the
    volume of the oil decreases by 2×10^{-8} m^3, the applied pressure
    must be approximately
    (a) 17 Pa   (b) 68 Pa   (c) 0.06 Pa   (d) 1.7×10^{17} Pa

COMPLETION QUESTIONS

1. Three types of stress are _____ stress, _____
   stress, and _____ stress.

2. The constant ratio of stress to strain is called the _____
   _____.

63

3. _____ is the relative change in the dimensions or shape of a body as a result of an applied force.

4. Whenever a shearing stress is applied, the strain can be approximated by _____.

5. The reciprocal of the bulk modulus is called the _____ _____ and is denoted by the symbol _____.

6. The stress on a body is the ratio of _____ to _____.

7. The ultimate strength of a material is always _____ _____ its elastic limit.

8. Provided that the _____ is not exceeded, an elastic strain is directly proportional to the _____ _____. This is a statement of _____ law.

9. The term *elastic limit* refers to the maximum _____ a body can experience without becoming permanently deformed.

10. The only elastic modulus which applies for liquids is the _____.

ANSWERS TO TRUE-FALSE, MULTIPLE CHOICE, AND COMPLETION QUESTIONS

1. False	1. c	1.	tensile, compressure, shearing
2. False	2. a	2.	modulus of elasticity
3. True	3. d	3.	strain
4. True	4. b	4.	tan ϕ
5. True	5. d	5.	compressibility, k
6. True	6. b	6.	applied force, surface area
7. False	7. b	7.	greater than
8. True	8. a	8.	elastic limit, applied stress,
9. True	9. c		Hooke's
10. True	10. a	9.	stress
		10.	bulk modulus

CHAPTER 14. SIMPLE HARMONIC MOTION

CONTENTS

OBJECTIVES

You should be able to:

1. Give two examples which approximate simple harmonic motion and in each case state why the motion is not exactly harmonic.

2. Describe the relationship between *force* and *displacement* in simple harmonic motion.

3. Construct figures similar to Figs. 14-4, 14-5*b*, and 14-6*b* to illustrate your understanding of the *reference circle* as an aid in describing simple harmonic motion.

4. Describe briefly how the magnitude and direction of the velocity vary as a function of time in simple harmonic motion.

5. Describe briefly how the magnitude and direction of the acceleration vary as a function of time in simple harmonic motion.

6. Solve for the displacement x, the velocity v, or the acceleration a when the time, the frequency, and the amplitude in simple harmonic motion are given.

7. Compute the frequency or period when the position and acceleration of an object at any instant during simple harmonic motion are given.

8. Write and apply a relationship between the frequency of motion and the mass of a vibrating object when the spring constant is known.

9. Construct a simple pendulum from a mass and a supply of string which will oscillate with an assigned period.

DEFINITIONS

Periodic motion - Motion in which a body moves back and forth over a fixed path, returning to each position and velocity after a definite interval of time.

Simple harmonic motion - Periodic motion, in the absence of friction, produced by a restoring force which is directly proportional to the displacement and oppositely directed.

Restoring force - The elastic force which always tends to restore a vibrating body to its equilibrium position.

Reference circle - An imaginary circle drawn in order to relate simple harmonic motion to analogous uniform circular motion.

Period - The time required for one complete oscillation.

Frequency - The number of complete oscillations per unit of time. The frequency is the reciprocal of the period.

Amplitude - In simple harmonic motion, the maximum displacement in either direction from the equilibrium position.

Displacement - In simple harmonic motion, the displacement from the equilibrium position at a particular instant.

Simple pendulum - An ideal pendulum for which all the mass is concentrated at the center of gravity of the bob and the restoring force acts at a single point.

Torsion pendulum - A solid disk or cylinder supported at the end of a thin rod or wire.

Torsion constant - A property of a material which is equal to the negative ratio of the restoring torque to the angle of twist for a torsion pendulum.

PHYSICAL CONCEPTS

1. Simple harmonic motion is periodic motion, in the absence of friction, under the influence of a *restoring force F* given by

$$\overline{F = -kx} \qquad \text{restoring force}$$

2. Since $F = ma = -kx$, the acceleration produced by a restoring force is

$$a = -\frac{k}{m}x \qquad \text{acceleration due to restoring force}$$

3. A convenient way to study simple harmonic motion is to use the reference circle. The variation in displacement x, velocity v, and acceleration a during simple harmonic motion can be visualized from Fig. 14-1. These quantities are expressed in terms of the amplitude A, the frequency f, and the time t. Thus, the following equations apply for simple harmonic motion:

66

$x = A \cos 2\pi f t$ displacement

$v = -2\pi f A \sin 2\pi f t$ velocity

$a = -4\pi^2 f^2 x$ acceleration

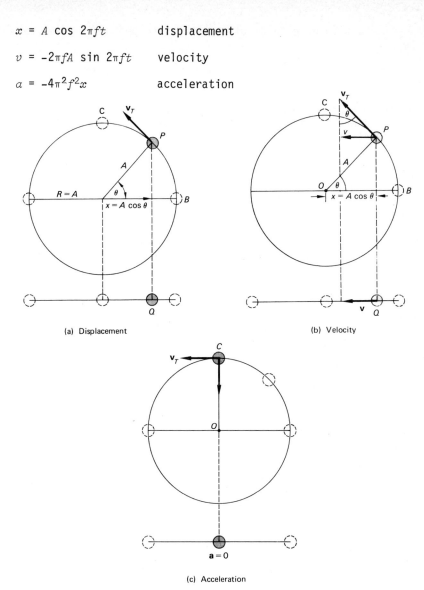

(a) Displacement

(b) Velocity

(c) Acceleration

Fig. 14-1.   The reference circle.

4. The period T and the frequency f in simple harmonic motion are found from

$$f = \frac{1}{2\pi} \sqrt{-\frac{a}{x}}$$ or $$f = \frac{1}{2\pi} \sqrt{\frac{k}{m}}$$ frequency

$$T = 2\pi \sqrt{-\frac{x}{a}}$$ or $$T = 2\pi \sqrt{\frac{m}{k}}$$ period

5. For a simple pendulum of length l, the period is given by

$$T = 2\pi \sqrt{-\frac{l}{g}} \qquad \text{period of simple pendulum}$$

6. A torsion pendulum consists of a solid disk or cylinder of moment of inertia I suspended at the end of a thin rod. If the torsion constant k' is known, the period is given by

$$T = 2\pi \sqrt{\frac{I}{k'}} \qquad \text{period of torsion pendulum}$$

TRUE-FALSE QUESTIONS

T F 1. When an object is vibrating with simple harmonic motion, its acceleration is a minimum when it passes through its equilibrium position.

T F 2. Simple harmonic motion is realized only in the absence of friction.

T F 3. In simple harmonic motion, the velocity is greatest when the oscillating body reaches its amplitude.

T F 4. The greater the period of vibration, the greater the maximum acceleration of a body vibrating with simple harmonic motion.

T F 5. The maximum velocity in simple harmonic motion occurs when the angle on the reference circle is 90 or 270°.

T F 6. In simple harmonic motion, the acceleration is quadrupled when the frequency is increased by a factor of 2.

T F 7. Since the acceleration due to gravity is less at higher elevations, the length of a pendulum in a pendulum clock should be shortened.

T F 8. For a torsion pendulum, increasing the moment of inertia of the vibrating disk will also increase the frequency of vibration.

T F 9. The acceleration of a harmonic oscillator is a function of displacement but independent of amplitude.

T F 10. The velocity of a harmonic oscillator depends on the frequency of vibration but is independent of amplitude.

MULTIPLE-CHOICE QUESTIONS

1. If the frequency doesn't change in simple harmonic motion, the acceleration of a mass is directly proportional to its
   (a) velocity (b) displacement (c) mass (d) amplitude

2. In simple harmonic motion, the velocity at any instant is not a function of the
   (a) period (b) amplitude (c) time (d) frequency

3. In simple harmonic motion, the radius of the reference circle corresponds most closely with the actual
   (a) displacement (b) velocity
   (c) amplitude (d) period

4. The period of pendulum is determined by its
   (a) maximum speed (b) length
   (c) amplitude (d) mass

5. A body vibrating with simple harmonic motion experiences its maximum restoring force when it is at its
   (a) equilibrium position (b) amplitude
   (c) greatest speed (d) least acceleration

6. A 2-kg mass m moves in simple harmonic motion with a frequency f. What mass will cause the system to vibrate with twice the frequency?
   (a) 0.5 kg (b) 4 kg (c) 8 kg (d) 16 kg

7. At the instant a harmonic oscillator has a displacement of -8 cm, its acceleration is 2 cm/s^2. The period is
   (a) 8π s (b) 4π s (c) 2π s (d) π s

8. A harmonic oscillator vibrates with a frequency of 4 Hz and an amplitude of 2 cm. Its maximum velocity is
   (a) 2π cm/s (b) 4π cm/s (c) 8π cm/s (d) 16π cm/s

9. In the above problem, the maximum acceleration is
   (a) $256\pi^2$ cm/s^2 (b) $128\pi^2$ cm/s^2
   (c) $64\pi^2$ cm/s^2 (d) $32\pi^2$ cm/s^2

10. A 2-kg steel ball is attached to the end of a flat strip of metal that is clamped at its base. If the spring constant is 8 N/m, the frequency of vibration will be approximately
    (a) 0.08 Hz (b) 0.16 Hz (c) 0.32 Hz (d) 0.64 Hz

COMPLETION QUESTIONS

1. The _____ is used to compare the motion of an object moving in a circle with its horizontal projection.

2. In simple harmonic motion, when the displacement is a maximum the
_____ is zero and the _____ is
a maximum.

3. The product of the amplitude and the cosine of the reference
angle is the _____ of a body vibrating with simple
harmonic motion.

4. The _____ and therefore the
_____ of a vibrating object is zero at the
center of oscillation.

5. In simple harmonic motion, the _____ and the
_____ are always opposite in sign.

6. In order to calculate the period for a torsion pendulum, we must
know the _____ of the disk and the
_____.

7. The period can be computed if the acceleration is known at a
particular _____.

8. In simple harmonic motion, the restoring force which is directly
proportional to the _____ and _____ in direc-
tion.

9. If the frequency f is to be calculated from the known spring constant k, we must know the _____ of the vibrating body.

10. In order for the vibration of a pendulum to approximate simple
harmonic motion, the _____
must be small.

ANSWERS TO TRUE-FALSE, MULTIPLE CHOICE, AND COMPLETION QUESTIONS

1.	True	1.	b	1.	reference circle
2.	True	2.	a	2.	velocity, acceleration
3.	False	3.	c	3.	displacement
4.	False	4.	b	4.	restoring force, acceleration
5.	True	5.	b	5.	displacement, acceleration
6.	True	6.	a	6.	moment of inertia, torsion
7.	True	7.	b		constant
8.	True	8.	d	7.	torsion constant
9.	True	9.	b	8.	displacement, opposite
10.	False	10.	c	9.	mass
				10.	amplitude or angle

CHAPTER 15. FLUIDS AT REST

CONTENTS

1. Density
2. Pressure
3. Fluid Pressure
4. Measuring Pressure
5. The Hydraulic Press
6. Archimedes' Principle

OBJECTIVES

You should be able to:

1. Distinguish by example and discussion between *weight* and *mass density*.

2. Compute the density of a solid of regular shape with an analytical balance.

3. Define and apply the concept of *pressure* to the solution of physical problems.

4. Write in your own words the four principles summarized in the section on fluid pressure (Sec. 15-3) and after each principle, draw a sketch to illustrate your interpretation of that principle.

5. Write a physical relationship expressing fluid pressure as a function of depth and density of the fluid and if two of these parameters are given, solve for the other in a physical problem.

6. Write and illustrate two applications of Pascal's law.

7. Define *absolute pressure, gauge pressure,* and *atmospheric pressure* and write an example demonstrating the relationship between these terms.

8. Write and apply formulas for calculating the mechanical advantage of a hydraulic press in terms of input and output forces, or areas.

9. Write in your own words a statement of *Archimedes' principle* and write the principle as a mathematical equation.

10. Use Archimedes' principle to determine the mass of a floating object with an analytical balance and a beaker of water with an overflow spout.

11. Apply the concepts presented in this chapter to the solution of problems similar to examples presented in the text.

DEFINITIONS

Weight density - The ratio of an object's weight to its volume. It depends upon the acceleration due to gravity.

Mass density - The ratio of an object's mass to its volume. It represents a universal constant for a given material.

Pressure - The perpendicular force per unit of area.

Total force - For a given surface, the sum of all the forces acting on that surface.

Pascal's law - An external pressure applied to an enclosed fluid is transmitted uniformly throughout the volume of the liquid.

Absolute pressure - The total fluid pressure, including atmospheric pressure.

Gauge pressure - The difference between absolute pressure and atmospheric pressure. Most devices which measure pressure actually indicate gauge pressures.

Manometer - An open U-shaped tube partially filled with a liquid (usually mercury). When one end of the tube is connected to a pressurized chamber and the other end is left open, the difference in the levels of the liquid is an indication of gauge pressure.

Archimedes' principle - An object which is completely or partly submerged in a fluid experiences an upward force equal to the weight of the fluid displaced.

Buoyant force - The upward force in Archimedes' principle which is equal to the weight of the displaced fluid.

PHYSICAL CONCEPTS

1. A very important physical property of matter is its *density*. The weight density D and the mass density ρ are defined as follows:

$$Weight\ density = \frac{weight}{volume} \qquad \boxed{D = \frac{W}{V}} \qquad N/m^3 \text{ or } lb/ft^3$$

$$Mass\ density = \frac{mass}{volume} \qquad \boxed{\rho = \frac{m}{V}} \qquad kg/m^3 \text{ or } slugs/ft^3$$

Since $W = mg$, the relationship between D and ρ is

$$\boxed{D = \rho g} \qquad weight\ density = mass\ density \times gravity$$

2. Important points to remember about fluid pressure:

   (a) *The forces exerted by a fluid on the walls of its container are always perpendicular.*

   (b) *The fluid pressure is directly proportional to the depth of the fluid and to its density.*

   $$P = \frac{F}{A} \qquad P = Dh \qquad P = \rho gh$$

   (c) *At any particular depth, the fluid pressure is the same in all directions.*

   (d) *Fluid pressure is independent of the shape or area of its container.*

3. Pascal's law states that *an external pressure applied to an enclosed fluid is transmitted uniformly throughout the volume of the liquid.*

4. When measurements of fluid pressure are made it is essential to distinguish between *absolute* pressure and *gauge* pressure:

   Absolute pressure = gauge pressure + atmospheric pressure

   $$\text{Atmospheric pressure} = 1 \text{ atm} = 1.013 \times 10^5 \text{ N/m}^2$$
   $$= 1.013 \times 10^5 \text{ Pa} = 14.7 \text{ lb/in.}^2$$
   $$= 76 \text{ cm of mercury}$$

5. Pascal's law applied to the hydraulic press gives the following for the ideal advantage (see Fig. 15-1):

   $$M_I = \frac{F_o}{F_i} = \frac{s_i}{s_o}$$

   Ideal mechanical advantage for hydraulic press

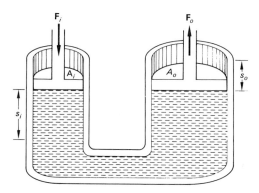

Fig. 15-1. The hydraulic press.

6. **Archimedes' principle:** *an object which is completely or partly submerged in a fluid experiences an upward force equal to the weight of the fluid displaced.*

$$\overline{F_B = mg} \qquad \text{or} \qquad \overline{F_B = V\rho g} \qquad \text{buoyant force}$$

TRUE-FALSE QUESTIONS

T   F   1.   The fluid pressure at the bottom of a container depends on the area of the bottom as well as the height of the fluid.

T   F   2.   Fluid pressure is independent of the shape or size of the container.

T   F   3.   At a particular depth in a liquid, the fluid pressure is the same in all directions except the upward direction.

T   F   4.   Pascal's law states that the buoyant force will always be equal to the weight of the displaced fluid.

T   F   5.   If a rock has a density of 4 kg/m^3 on the earth, it will have a density of 4 kg/m^3 on the moon.

T   F   6.   Since the weight of the overlying fluid in a container is proportional to its density, the pressure at any depth is also proportional to the density of the fluid.

T   F   7.   The buoyant force is equal to the resultant force acting on a submerged object.

T   F   8.   The buoyant force on a weather balloon does not depend directly on the density of the gas inside the balloon.

T   F   9.   The smaller the area of the input cylinder of a hydraulic press in comparison with the area of the output cylinder the larger the mechanical advantage.

T   F   10.   An open-tube manometer is a device used to measure absolute pressure.

MULTIPLE-CHOICE QUESTIONS

1. Which of the following is independent of the density of a liquid?
   (a) the total force at the bottom of the container
   (b) the pressure at the surface of the liquid
   (c) the pressure at the bottom of the container
   (d) the pressure at the sides of the container

2. The hydraulic press operates primarily on
   (a) Archimedes' principle   (b) Pascal's law
   (c) Boyle's law   (d) Newton's laws

3. The ratio of an object's weight density to its mass density is
   (a) absolute pressure   (b) less than 1
   (c) equal to g (d) unitless

4. The fluid pressure at any point in a liquid is
   (a) proportional to its density
   (b) of the same magnitude
   (c) independent of height
   (d) directed downward only

5. An open-tube manometer measures
   (a) atmospheric pressure   (b) absolute pressure
   (c) gauge pressure   (d) sea-level pressure

6. A cork float has a volume of 2 ft^3 and a density of 12 lb/ft^3. Its weight is
   (a) 6 lb   (b) 24 lb   (c) 0.17 lb   (d) 12 lb

7. Gasoline has a density of 680 kg/m^3. The pressure at the bottom of a container filled with gasoline to a height of 2 m is approximately
   (a) 1360 N/m^2 (b) 3400 N/m^2 (c) 13,328 N/m^2 (d) 1500 N/m^2

8. A square chunk of cork weighing 2 N floats with exactly half its volume submerged in water. The weight of the displaced water is
   (a) 4 N   (b) 2 N   (c) 1 N   (d) 0.5 N

9. A force of 600 lb is applied to the small piston of a hydraulic press. The diameter of the input piston is exactly one-half the diameter of the output piston. The lifting force exerted by the output piston is
   (a) 150 lb   (b) 300 lb   (c) 1200 lb   (d) 2400 lb

10. What must the volume of a balloon be if it is to support a total mass of 1000 kg at a point where the density of air is 1.2 kg/m^3? (The total mass includes that of the balloon and the helium with which it is filled, as well as the payload.)
    (a) 85 m^3 (b) 833 m^3 (c) 1200 m^3 (d) 8166 m^3

COMPLETION QUESTIONS

1. Gauge pressure is _____ pressure less _____ pressure.

2. The forces exerted by a fluid on the walls of its container are always _____.

3. The fluid pressure is directly proportional to the _____ of the fluid and to its _____.

75

4. Fluid pressure is independent of the _____ or _____ of its container.

5. The weight density of a body is equal to the ratio of its _____ to its _____. Is it a universal constant for a given material? _____.

6. An object which is completely or partly submerged in a fluid experiences an upward force, called the _____ force, which is equal to the _____ of the fluid displaced. This is _____ principle.

7. An open, U-shaped tube partially filled with mercury can be used to measure _____ pressure. Such a device is called a _____.

8. If the weight of the displaced fluid exceeds the weight of a submerged body, the body will _____.

9. The _____ press operates on the principle that an output pressure is essentially equal to an input pressure. This principle was named after _____.

10. The ideal mechanical advantage for a hydraulic press is the ratio of the _____ of the output piston to that of the input piston.

ANSWERS TO TRUE-FALSE, MULTIPLE CHOICE, AND COMPLETION QUESTIONS

1.	False	1.	b	1.	absolute, atmosphere
2.	True	2.	b	2.	perpendicular
3.	False	3.	c	3.	depth, density
4.	False	4.	a	4.	shape, area
5.	True	5.	c	5.	weight, volume, no
6.	True	6.	b	6.	buoyant, weight, Archimedes'
7.	False	7.	c	7.	gauge, manometer
8.	True	8.	b	8.	rise to the surface and float
9.	True	9.	d	9.	hydraulic, Pascal
10.	False	10.	b	10.	area

CHAPTER 16.   FLUIDS IN MOTION

CONTENTS

1. Fluid Flow
2. Pressure and Velocity
3. Bernoulli's Equation

4. Applications of Bernoulli's Equation

OBJECTIVES

You should be able to:

1. Define and demonstrate what is meant by *streamline flow* and *turbulent flow*.

2. Define *rate of flow* as it applies to fluids and write an equation that relates rate of flow to velocity and cross-sectional area.

3. Predict the change in velocity of a fluid as the cross-sectional area of a pipe changes.

4. Describe or perform two experiments which demonstrate the decrease in pressure as a result of an increase in fluid velocity.

5. Write *Bernoulli's equation* in its general form and describe the equation as it would apply to (a) a fluid at rest, (b) fluid flow at constant pressure, and (c) flow through a horizontal pipe.

6. Apply Bernoulli's equation to the solution of problems involving absolute pressure P, density ρ, fluid elevation h, and fluid velocity v.

7. Describe or perform an experiment demonstrating (a) Torricelli's theorem and (b) the Venturi effect.

DEFINITIONS

Streamline flow - Motion of a fluid in which every particle in the fluid follows the same path (past a particular point) as that followed by previous particles.

Turbulent flow - Fluid motion in which streamlines break down as obstacles are encountered, setting up swirls and eddies.

Rate of flow - The volume of fluid that passes a certain cross section per unit of time.

Venturi effect - The principle by which a drop in pressure occurs due to the increased velocity of a fluid flowing through a constriction.

Bernoulli's principle - A statement of the law of conservation of
energy for the steady flow of an incompressible fluid. For every
unit of volume, the sum of pressure, kinetic energy, and potential
energy is a constant.

Torricelli's theorem - The emergent velocity of a fluid at a depth h
is equal to the square root of twice the product of h and the
acceleration due to gravity.

PHYSICAL CONCEPTS

1. The *rate of flow* is defined as the volume of fluid that passes a
    certain cross section A per unit of time t. In terms of fluid
    velocity v, we write

    $$R = \frac{V}{t} = vA \qquad rate\ of\ flow = velocity \times cross\ section$$

2. For an incompressible fluid flowing through pipes in which the
    cross sections vary, the rate of flow is constant:

    $$v_1 A_1 = v_2 A_2 \qquad d_1^2 v_1 = d_2^2 v_2$$

    When v is the fluid velocity, A is the cross-sectional area of
    the pipe, and d is the diameter of the pipe.

3. The net work done on a fluid is equal to the changes in kinetic
    and potential energy of the fluid. Bernoulli's equation expresses
    this fact in terms of the pressure P, the density ρ, the height
    of the fluid h, and its velocity v.

    $$P + \rho g h + \tfrac{1}{2}\rho v^2 = constant \qquad \text{Bernoulli's equation}$$

    If a volume of fluid changes from a state 1 to a state 2, as
    shown in Fig. 16-1, we can write

    $$P_1 + \rho g h_1 + \tfrac{1}{2}\rho v_1^2 = P_2 + \rho g h_2 + \tfrac{1}{2}\rho v_2^2$$

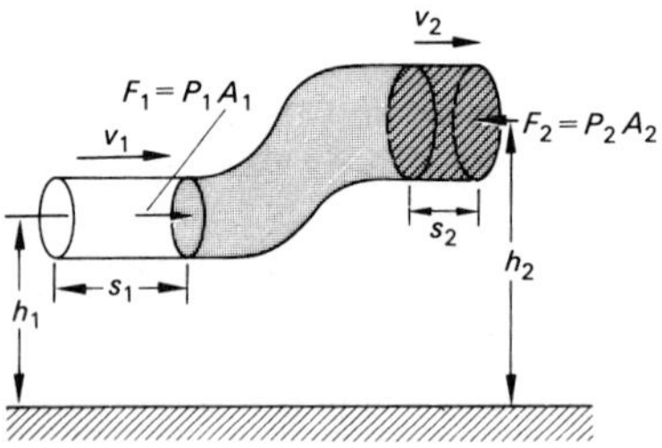

Fig. 16-1. Deriving Bernoulli's equation.

4. Special applications of Bernoulli's equation occur when one of the parameters does not change:

For a stationary liquid
$(v_1 = v_2)$

$$P_2 - P_1 = \rho g(h_1 - h_2)$$

If the pressure is constant
$(P_1 = P_2)$

$$v = \sqrt{2gh}$$

For a horizontal pipe
$(h_1 = h_2)$

$$P_1 + \tfrac{1}{2}\rho v_1{}^2 = P_2 + \tfrac{1}{2}\rho v_2{}^2$$

TRUE-FALSE QUESTIONS

T   F   1.   The rate of flow is defined as the speed with which a fluid passes a certain cross section.

T   F   2.   If a fluid is considered incompressible, and if we neglect internal friction, the rate of flow through a pipe remains constant even when the cross-sectional area changes.

T   F   3.   Decreasing the diameter of a pipe by one-half will cause the velocity of a fluid through the pipe to be quadrupled.

T   F   4.   An increase in fluid speed results in an increased pressure at the constriction in a venturi meter.

T   F   5.   The pressure P in Bernoulli's equation represents the absolute pressure and not the gauge pressure.

T   F   6.   Bernoulli's equation applies for fluids at rest as well as for fluids in motion.

T   F   7.   If several holes are cut in the side of a container filled with water, the discharge velocity increases with depth below the surface; however, the range is a maximum at the midpoint.

T   F   8.   If we consider a fluid to be incompressible and neglect the effects of friction, the change in velocity as a fluid goes through the constriction in a horizontal venturi tube does not depend on the density of the fluid.

T   F   9.   Either weight density or mass density may be used in Bernoulli's equation.

T   F   10.   Torricelli's theorem might be thought of as a special case of the more general Bernoulli's equation.

MULTIPLE-CHOICE QUESTIONS

1. The rate of flow of a fluid out of an opening at the bottom of a container does not depend on
   (a) the depth of the hole   (b) the area of the opening
   (c) the density of the fluid   (d) the acceleration of gravity

2. The product of velocity and cross-sectional area for a liquid flowing through a pipe is a measure of the
   (a) rate of flow   (b) fluid pressure
   (c) volume of fluid   (d) none of these

3. The speed of discharge of a fluid through an orifice is most closely associated with
   (a) Bernoulli   (b) Torricelli
   (c) Venturi   (d) Archimedes

4. When one blows air across the top of a sheet of paper, the paper rises due to the
   (a) force of the blow
   (b) drop in pressure above the paper
   (c) increase in pressure below the paper
   (d) increase in temperature of the air

5. When there is no change in pressure at the beginning and end of a flow process, Bernoulli's equation reduces to
   (a) $P = \rho g h$ (b) $P + \frac{1}{2}\rho v^2 = $ constant
   (c) $v = \sqrt{2gh}$ (d) $\rho g h = $ constant

6. Water flowing at a speed of 20 cm/s in a 6-cm-diameter pipe encounters a constriction 3 cm in diameter. The speed through the constriction is
   (a) 80 cm/s   (b) 40 cm/s   (c) 5 cm/s   (d) 10 cm/s

7. A container 4 ft high is filled to the top with liquid. The discharge velocity from a hole at the bottom of the container is
   (a) 12 ft/s   (b) 16 ft/s   (c) 20 ft/s   (d) 24 ft/s

8. In a horizontal venturi tube, the pressure at the inlet is 27 lb/ft^2, and the velocity of a liquid flowing through it is 10 ft/s. The density of the liquid is 2 slugs/ft^3, and the pressure at the throat of the venturi drops to 6 lb/ft^2. The velocity of the liquid in the throat is approximately
   (a) 11 ft/s   (b) 15 ft/s   (c) 20 ft/s   (d) 25 ft/s

9. The dimensions of every terms in Bernoulli's equation are those of
   (a) length   (b) velocity   (c) density   (d) pressure

10. Water rushes out of the end of a pipe at the rate of 2 m^3/s and with a velocity of 4 m/s. The area of the opening is
    (a) 2 m^2 (b) 1 m^2 (c) 0.5 m^2 (d) 0.25 m^2

COMPLETION QUESTIONS

1. The _____ is defined as the volume of fluid that passes a certain cross section per unit of time. Its units are _____ in the Bgs.

2. The motion of a fluid in which every particle in the fluid follows the same path past a particular point as that followed by previous particles is called _____.

3. The _____ principle is responsible for mixing fuel with air in the throat of a carburetor as air rushes through it.

4. In our discussion of fluids, there are four physical quantities derived from the fundamental quantities of mass, length, and time which play important roles. They are _____, _____, _____, and _____.

5. The discharge velocity increases with _____ below the surface of a liquid. The range of the discharged liquid is a maximum at the _____.

6. The velocity of discharge from an orifice depends on the _____ and the _____. The magnitude of the velocity is predicted by _____ theorem.

7. The product of _____ and _____ is a constant and is a measure of the rate of flow.

8. Fluid flow in which swirls and eddies increase the frictional drag is called _____ flow.

9. In applying Bernoulli's equation, it must be remembered that P represents _____ pressure and ρ represents _____ density.

10. In Bernoulli's equation, the sum of _____, _____, and _____ must remain constant.

ANSWERS TO TRUE-FALSE, MULTIPLE CHOICE, AND COMPLETION QUESTIONS

1. False	1. c	1. rate of flow, ft^3/s
2. True	2. a	2. streamline flow
3. True	3. b	3. venturi
4. False	4. b	4. pressure, velocity, density,
5. True	5. c	height
6. True	6. a	5. depth, midpoint
7. True	7. b	6. depth, acceleration of gravity,
8. True	8. a	Torricelli's
9. False	9. d	7. cross-sectional area, velocity
10. True	10. c	8. turbulent
		9. absolute, mass
		10. P, ρgh, $\frac{1}{2}\rho v^2$

CHAPTER 17.   TEMPERATURE AND EXPANSION

CONTENTS

OBJECTIVES

You should be able to:

1. Demonstrate by example or experiment your understanding of the distinction between *thermal energy* and *temperature*.

2. Demonstrate by example or experiment your understanding of the distinction between a *specific* temperature and a temperature *interval*.

3. Explain, in 25 words or less, the concept of *thermal equilibrium*.

4. Demonstrate your familiarity with the *Celsius, Fahrenheit, Kelvin,* and *Rankine* temperature scales by converting from specific temperatures on one scale to corresponding temperatures on another scale.

5. Convert a temperature interval on the Fahrenheit or Rankine scale to the corresponding interval in Celsius degrees or in kelvins.

6. Describe an experiment which illustrates the meaning of *absolute zero*.

7. Graduate an unmarked mercury-in-glass thermometer in Celsius degrees given the equipment normally available in a physics laboratory.

8. Predict the change in length of a metal rod of known length and material as the rod is heated through a known temperature interval.

9. Design an experiment to determine the coefficient of linear expansion for a solid metal rod.

10. Rank at least four of five common metals in order of increasing linear expansion coefficients.

11. Describe an experiment which illustrates your understanding of the overall expansion of a heated metal ring.

12. Predict the volume overflow when a container of known volume and material filled with a given liquid is heated through a given temperature interval.

DEFINITIONS

Thermal energy - The total internal energy of an object, i.e., the sum of its molecular kinetic and potential energies.

Thermal equilibrium - Two objects are said to be in thermal equilibrium if and only if they have the same temperature.

Temperature - The degree of hotness or coldness as measured on a definite scale.

Thermometer - A device which through marked scales can give an indication of its own temperature.

Ice point - The temperature at which water and ice coexist in thermal equilibrium under a pressure of 1 atm (0°C or 32°F).

Steam point - The temperature at which water and steam coexist in thermal equilibrium under a pressure of 1 atm (100°C or 212°F).

Celsius scale - A temperature scale which assigns the number 0 to the ice point and the number 100 to the steam point.

Fahrenheit scale - A temperature scale on which the ice point is assigned the number 32 and the steam point is assigned the number 212.

Absolute zero - The true zero of temperature. The temperature at which the volume of an ideal gas would be zero.

Kelvin scale - An absolute temperature scale based on the same intervals as the Celsius scale except that its zero point is at -273°C.

Rankine scale - An absolute temperature scale based on the same intervals as the Fahrenheit scale except that its zero point is at -460°F.

Constant-volume thermometer - A gas thermometer which maintains constant volume and uses changes in pressure to indicate temperature.

Constant-pressure thermometer - A gas thermometer which maintains a constant pressure and utilizes changes in volume as an indicator of temperature.

Coefficient of linear expansion - A property of a material which determines the change in length per unit length per degree change in temperature.

PHYSICAL CONCEPTS

1. There are four commonly used temperature scales that you should be thoroughly familiar with. These scales are compared in Fig. 17-1, giving values for the steam point, the ice point, and absolute zero on each scale. It is very important for you to distinguish between a temperature interval Δt and a specific temperature t. For temperature intervals:

$$\frac{5\ C°}{9\ F°} = 1 = \frac{9\ F°}{5\ C°} \qquad 1\ K = 1\ C° \qquad 1\ R° = 1\ F° \qquad \text{temperature intervals}$$

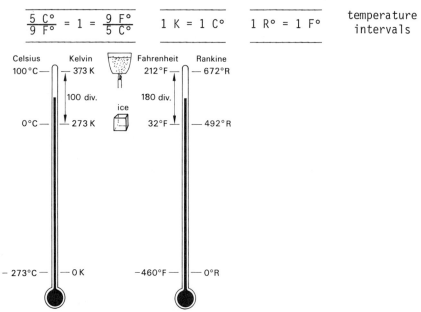

Fig. 17-1. A comparison of the four commonly used temperature scales.

2. For specific temperatures you must correct for the interval difference, but you must also correct for the fact that different numbers are assigned for the same temperatures:

$$t_C = \frac{5}{9}(t_F - 32) \qquad t_F = \frac{9}{5}t_C + 32 \qquad \text{specific temperatures}$$

$$T_K = t_C + 273 \qquad T_R = t_F + 460 \qquad \text{absolute temperatures}$$

3. The following relations apply for thermal expansion of solids:

$$\Delta L = \alpha L_0\ \Delta t \qquad L = L_0 + \alpha L_0\ \Delta t \qquad \text{linear expansion}$$

$$\Delta A = \gamma A_0\ \Delta t \qquad A = A_0 + \gamma A_0\ \Delta t \qquad \gamma = 2\alpha \qquad \text{area expansion}$$

$$\Delta V = \beta V_0\ \Delta t \qquad V = V_0 + \beta V_0\ \Delta t \qquad \beta = 3\alpha \qquad \text{volume expansion}$$

84

4. The volume expansion of a liquid uses the same relation as for a solid except, of course, that there is no linear expansion coefficient α for a liquid. Only β is needed.

TRUE-FALSE QUESTIONS

T   F   1. Two objects which have the same temperature also have the same thermal energy.

T   F   2. Two objects are said to be in thermal equilibrium if and only if they are at the same temperature.

T   F   3. Twenty Celsius degrees represents the same temperature interval as twenty kelvins.

T   F   4. Water freezes at 460° on the Rankine scale.

T   F   5. When converting a temperature interval from degrees Rankine to kelvins, the number of Rankine degrees should be multiplied by 5/9.

T   F   6. When converting a specific temperature in degrees Fahrenheit to the corresponding temperature in degrees Celsius, the number is multiplied by 9/5 and added to 32.

T   F   7. For a given temperature interval, the same linear-expansion coefficient may be used for the same material regardless of the choice of units for length.

T   F   8. For a solid disk with a hole in its center, the diameter of the disk and the diameter of the hole will increase in length per unit length at a rate given by its linear expansion coefficient.

T   F   9. The volume-expansion coefficient for a solid is approximately equal to 3 times the linear-expansion coefficient, but this does not represent a true equality.

T   F   10. The temperature at the bottom of a frozen lake of fresh water is 4°C.

MULTIPLE-CHOICE QUESTIONS

1. Which of the following represents the steam point for water?
   (a) 100°F   (b) 212°C   (c) 273 K   (d) 672°R

2. Which of the following represents the largest temperature interval?
   (a) 40 F°   (b) 30 K   (c) 50 R°   (d) 20 C°

3. Two objects are in thermal equilibrium when they have the same
   (a) kinetic energy   (b) temperature
   (c) thermal energy   (d) potential energy

4. Which of the following represents the smallest specific temperature?
   (a) 40°F   (b) 5°F   (c) 510°R   (d) 280 K

5. The coefficient of linear expansion will vary only with a change in
   (a) temperature   (b) initial length
   (c) thermal energy   (d) material

6. When a flame is held to the bulb of a mercury-in-glass thermometer, the mercury level will
   (a) rise   (b) drop
   (c) drop and then rise   (d) rise and then drop

7. The boiling point of oxygen is -183°C. This temperature is also
   (a) -329.4°F   (b) 162.6°R   (c) 456 K   (d) -83.9°F

8. The linear-expansion coefficient for silver is $2 \times 10^{-5}/C°$. A 6-in. bar of silver is heated from 0 to 100°C. The increase in length is approximately
   (a) 0.06 in.   (b) 0.12 in.   (c) 0.012 in.   (d) 0.006 in.

9. The area-expansion coefficient for the silver bar in the above problem is approximately
   (a) $1 \times 10^{-5}/F°$ (b) $4 \times 10^{-5}/F°$
   (c) $7.2 \times 10^{-5}/F°$ (d) $2.2 \times 10^{-5}/F°$

10. The volume-expansion coefficient for ethyl alcohol is $11 \times 10^{-4}/C°$. What change in temperature must occur in order to increase the volume of 16 liters of the alcohol to 17 liters?
    (a) 56.8 C°   (b) 1454 C°   (c) 53.5 C°   (d) 90.9 C°

COMPLETION QUESTIONS

1. The temperature at which the volume of an ideal gas is zero is referred to as _____.

2. Temperature is a measure of the _____ _____ per molecule, and two objects which are at the same temperature are in _____.

3. A metal bar 1 ft in length increases its length by 0.0006 ft when its temperature is increased by 1 C°. Under the same conditions, a 1-m length of the same material would increase its length by _____ m.

4. The coefficient of linear expansion may be defined as the change in _____ per unit _____ per degree rise in _____.

5. A device which can give an indication of its own temperature is called a _____.

6. The temperature interval on the Kelvin scale is the same as the
   _____ temperature interval; however, it is larger by
   a factor of _____ than the Fahrenheit interval.

7. Two fixed points often used as standards for calibration of
   thermometers are the _____ and the
   _____.

8. One hundred eighty divisions on the Fahrenheit scale would corres-
   spond to _____ divisions on the Kelvin
   scale.

9. Thermal energy represents the sum of the _____
   _____ and _____ of all
   molecules present in a substance.

10. Water experiences its maximum _____ at 4°C.

ANSWERS TO TRUE-FALSE, MULTIPLE CHOICE, AND COMPLETION QUESTIONS

1.	False	1.	d	1.	absolute zero
2.	True	2.	b	2.	average kinetic energy,
3.	True	3.	b			thermal equilibrium
4.	False	4.	a	3.	0.0006
5.	True	5.	d	4.	length, length, temperature
6.	False	6.	c	5.	thermometer
7.	True	7.	b	6.	Celsius, 9/5
8.	True	8.	c	7.	ice point, steam point
9.	True	9.	d	8.	one hundred
10.	True	10.	a	9.	kinetic energy, potential
					energy
				10.	density

CHAPTER 18. QUANTITY OF HEAT

CONTENTS

OBJECTIVES

You should be able to:

1. Demonstrate by example or experiment your understanding of heat as a form of energy.

2. Represent the heat gained or lost in a given process in terms of the *calorie*, the *kilocalorie*, and the *Btu* as standard units.

3. Give an example illustrating the distinction between *quantity of heat* and *temperature*.

4. Demonstrate by example or experiment your understanding of *specific heat capacity* and its distinction from *heat capacity*.

5. Explain practical advantages or disadvantages of metals with large specific heat capacities.

6. Apply the *law of conservation of heat energy* to a given process in order to determine unknown parameters such as mass, specific heat, temperature, or latent heat of fusion.

7. Use your understanding of molecular kinetic and potential energies to describe the changes in phase which occur during the gain or loss of heat energy.

8. Design an experiment to measure the latent heat of fusion or vaporization for a given substance.

DEFINITIONS

Heat - A physical quantity which is a measure of the change in thermal energy during a given process.

Calorie - The quantity of heat required to change the temperature of one gram of water through one Celsius degree.

Kilocalorie - The quantity of heat required to change the temperature of one kilogram of water through one Celsius degree.

British thermal unit (Btu) - The quantity of heat required to change the temperature of one pound of water through one Fahrenheit degree.

Mechanical equivalent of heat - The quantitative relationship between thermal energy units and mechanical energy units:
1 Btu = 778 ft·lb; 1 cal = 4.186 J.

Heat capacity - The ratio of the heat supplied to a body to its corresponding rise in temperature.

Specific heat capacity - The quantity of heat required to change the temperature of a unit mass of a substance through one degree.

Conservation of heat energy - In any thermal process, the heat lost by warmer bodies must equal the heat gained by the cooler bodies.

Water equivalent - The mass of water which would gain or lose the same quantity of heat in a given process as a particular object, e.g., the water equivalent of a thermometer.

Fusion - The process in which the phase of a substance changes from a solid to a liquid. The opposite process is called *solidification*.

Melting point - The temperature at which fusion occurs at one atmosphere of pressure.

Latent heat of fusion - The quantity of heat per unit of mass required to change a substance from its solid phase to its liquid phase at its melting point. For water, L_f = 80 cal/g.

Vaporization - The process in which the phase of a substance changes from a liquid to a vapor. The opposite process is called *condensation*.

Boiling point - The temperature at which vaporization occurs under 1 atm of pressure.

Latent heat of vaporization - The quantity of heat per unit of mass required to change a substance from its liquid phase to its vapor phase at its boiling point.

Sublimation - The process in which the phase of a substance changes directly from a solid to a vapor without passing through the liquid phase.

Heat of combustion - The quantity of heat per unit mass or per unit volume liberated when a substance is burned.

PHYSICAL CONCEPTS

1. A unit of heat is the thermal energy required to produce a standard change. The *calorie*, the *kilocalorie*, and the *Btu*

are defined in the previous section. The following conversion factors are useful in problems involving thermal energy:

1 Btu = 252 cal = 0.252 kcal	1 cal = 4.186 J
1 Btu = 778 ft·lb	1 kcal = 4186 J

2. The specific heat capacity c is used to determine quantity of heat Q absorbed or released by a unit mass m as the temperature changes by an interval Δt.

$$c = \frac{Q}{m\ \Delta t} \qquad Q = mc\ \Delta t \qquad \text{specific heat capacity}$$

3. Conservation of thermal energy requires that in any exchange of thermal energy the heat lost must equal the heat gained.

$$\textit{Heat lost = heat gained} \qquad \Sigma(mc\ \Delta t)_{\text{loss}} = \Sigma(mc\ \Delta t)_{\text{gain}}$$

As an example, suppose body 1 transfers heat to bodies 2 and 3 as the system reaches an equilibrium temperature t_e:

$$m_1 c_1 (t_1 - t_e) = m_2 c_2 (t_e - t_2) + m_3 c_3 (t_e - t_3)$$

4. The latent heat of fusion L_f and the latent heat of vaporization L_v are heat losses or gains by a unit mass m during a phase change. There is no change in temperature.

$$L_f = \frac{Q}{m} \qquad Q = mL_f \qquad \text{latent heat of fusion}$$

$$L_v = \frac{Q}{m} \qquad Q = mL_v \qquad \text{latent heat of vaporization}$$

If a change of phase occurs, the above relationships must be added to the calorimetry equation as appropriate.

TRUE-FALSE QUESTIONS

T F 1. Since the Btu is based on the pound, its magnitude depends on the acceleration due to gravity.

T F 2. The Btu is a larger unit of heat than the kilocalorie.

T F 3. It is proper to speak of the heat capacity of a penny and the *specific* heat capacity of copper.

T F 4. The specific heat of any material is the same numerically in either the metric or British systems of units.

T F 5. A unit mass of water will absorb a larger quantity of heat per degree change in temperature than any other common substance.

T F 6. Since temperature is a measure of the average kinetic energy per molecule, the absorption or emission of thermal energy is always accompanied by a change in temperature.

T F 7. More than 5 times the thermal energy is required to vaporize 1 g of water than is required to melt 1 g of ice.

T F 8. Two objects which have the same heat capacity must be of the same material.

T F 9. The heat lost is equal to the heat gained unless a change of phase occurs.

T F 10. The mass of water displaced by a thermometer in a calorimetry experiment is known as the *water equivalent* of the thermometer.

MULTIPLE-CHOICE QUESTIONS

1. Which of the following is not a property of a material?
   (a) specific heat   (b) heat capacity
   (c) heat of fusion   (d) heat of combustion

2. Which of the following represents the largest transfer of heat?
   (a) 600 cal   (b) 3 Btu   (c) 0.7 kcal   (d) 2200 ft·lb

3. Which of the following is best associated with the term *heat*?
   (a) a change of temperature   (b) a change in kinetic energy
   (c) a change in thermal energy (d) a change in heat capacity

4. The specific heat of aluminum is 0.22 cal/g·C°. The quantity of heat required to change the temperature of 10 lb of aluminum from 20 to 100°F is approximately
   (a) 220 Btu   (b) 200 Btu   (c) 176 Btu   (d) 88 Btu

5. When a liquid freezes it
   (a) evolves heat   (b) absorbs heat
   (c) decreases in temperature   (d) sublimes

6. The quantity of heat required to convert 10 g of ice at 0°C to steam at 100°C is
   (a) 6300 cal   (b) 7200 cal   (c) 720 cal   (d) 1350 cal

7. If 50 g of aluminum shot (c = 0.22) is heated to 100°C and dropped into 200 g of water at 20°C, the equilibrium temperature (neglecting other heat transfers) is approximately
   (a) 24°C   (b) 26°C   (c) 34°C   (d) 46°C

8. A 50-g aluminum calorimeter cup is partially filled with 200 g of water at 20°C. What mass of copper (c = 0.093) at 100°C should be added to the system for the equilibrium temperature to be 30°C?
(a) 32.4 g   (b) 47.5 g   (c) 324 g   (d) 476 g

9. For a given substance, which of the following processes transfers the largest amount of thermal energy per unit of mass?
(a) fusion   (b) vaporization
(c) freezing   (d) sublimation

10. If 5 g of steam at 100°C is mixed with 10 g of ice at 0°C, the equilibrium mixture includes
(a) 3.33 g of steam and 11.67 g of water
(b) 1.67 g of steam and 13.33 g of water
(c) 1.67 g of steam and 3.33 g of water
(d) 15 g of water

COMPLETION QUESTIONS

1. The _____ is the quantity of heat required to change the temperature of one pound of water through one Fahrenheit degree.

2. The calorie is the quantity of heat required to change the _____ of _____ of water through one _____.

3. The quantity of heat per unit mass of a substance required to change its temperature through one degree is called its _____.

4. The latent heat of fusion of a substance is the _____
_____ necessary to change _____
_____ of the substance from a _____ to a
_____ at its _____.

5. The latent heat of vaporization is the heat per unit _____
of a substance required to change it from a _____ to
a _____ at its _____.

6. The _____ of _____ is the heat per unit mass required to burn a substance completely.

7. The latent heat of vaporization for water is _____ cal/g or _____ Btu/lb.

8. The process in which a substance changes directly from its solid phase to its vapor phase is called _____.

9. The quantitative relationship between thermal energy units and mechanical energy units is called _____
_____.

10. The conservation of heat energy states that in any given transfer of thermal energy the _____ must equal the _____.

ANSWERS TO TRUE-FALSE, MULTIPLE CHOICE, AND COMPLETION QUESTIONS

1. False	1. b	1. British thermal unit
2. False	2. b	2. temperature, one gram, Celsius degree
3. True	3. c	
4. True	4. c	3. specific heat capacity
5. True	5. a	4. quantity of heat, a unit mass, solid, liquid, melting point
6. False	6. b	
7. True	7. a	5. mass, liquid, vapor, boiling point
8. False	8. c	
9. False	9. d	6. heat, combustion
10. False	10. b	7. 540, 970
		8. sublimation
		9. the mechanical equivalent of heat
		10. heat lost, heat gained

CHAPTER 19. HEAT TRANSFER

CONTENTS

OBJECTIVES

You should be able to:

1. Demonstrate by example or experiment your understanding of *conduction, convection,* and *radiation.*

2. Design an experiment to determine the *thermal conductivity* of an unknown substance.

3. Give practical advantages and disadvantages of materials with large thermal conductivities.

4. Write a formula relating the quantity of heat Q transferred in a time τ to the material thickness L, the surface area A, and the difference in surface temperatures t.

5. State the units of thermal conductivity in either the Bgs or the metric system.

6. Solve thermal-conductivity problems for such parameters as quantity of heat Q, surface area A, surface temperatures t, time τ, and material thickness L.

7. Construct diagrams illustrating the convection currents for a fluid of known temperature which is in contact with a surface at a different temperature.

8. Explain how heat transfers by conduction, convection, and radiation are minimized in a common thermos jug.

9. Explain the significance of the *convection coefficient* and the part it plays in the design of heating or cooling systems.

10. Demonstrate by example or experiment your understanding of the rate of thermal radiation and its dependence on temperature.

11. Give two examples illustrating your understanding of the role played by *emissivity* in the transfer of heat by radiation.

12. Write the appropriate units for the rate of thermal radiation in the metric system of units.

DEFINITIONS

Conduction - The process in which heat energy is transferred by adjacent molecular collisions throughout a material medium. The medium itself does not move.

Convection - The process in which heat is transferred by the actual mass motion of a fluid.

Radiation - The process in which heat is transferred by electromagnetic waves.

Thermal conductivity - A measure of the ability of a substance to conduct heat.

Natural convection - Current produced in a fluid due to a difference in density which accompanies a change in temperature of a portion of the fluid.

Forced convection - Currents produced in a fluid due to the action of a pump, fan, or other device.

Convection coefficient - A property of the configuration or geometry of a solid which determines the rate of heat transfer by convection.

Blackbody radiation - Radiation emitted from an ideal radiator, which is defined as an object which absorbs *all* the radiation incident on its surface.

Emissivity - A measure of the ability of an object to absorb or emit thermal radiation.

Stefan-Boltzmann law - The relation predicting the power per unit of area emitted from an object of known emissivity and temperature.

Prevost's law of heat exchange - A body at the same temperature as its surroundings radiates and absorbs heat at the same rate.

PHYSICAL CONCEPTS

1. In the transfer of heat by conduction, the quantity of heat Q transferred per unit time τ through a wall or rod of length L is given by

$$H = \frac{Q}{\tau} = kA\frac{\Delta t}{L} \qquad \text{conduction}$$

metric units: kcal/s
Bgs units: Btu/h

where A is the area and Δt is the difference in surface temperatures. From this relation, the thermal conductivity is

$$k = \frac{QL}{A\tau\,\Delta t}$$

Metric units: kcal/m·s·C°
Bgs units: Btu·in./ft²·h·F°

95

2. The heat transferred by convection for a surface A is given by

$$H = \frac{Q}{\tau} = hA \, \Delta t \qquad \text{convection}$$

In this case Δt is the difference in temperature between the surface and the fluid. The convection coefficient for several cases is given below:

Geometry	kcal/$m^2 \cdot s \cdot C°$
Vertical plate	$(4.24 \times 10^{-4})\sqrt[4]{\Delta t}$
Horizontal plate, facing upward	$(5.95 \times 10^{-4})\sqrt[4]{\Delta t}$
Facing downward	$(3.14 \times 10^{-4})\sqrt[4]{\Delta t}$

3. For heat transfer by radiation, we define the rate of radiation as the energy emitted per unit area per unit time (or simply the power per unit area):

$$R = \frac{E}{\tau A} = \frac{P}{A} \qquad \text{rate of radiation, W/m}^2$$

According to *Stefan-Boltzmann's law*, this rate is given by

$$R = \frac{P}{A} = e\sigma T^4 \qquad \sigma = 5.67 \times 10^{-8} \text{ W/m}^2 \cdot K^4$$

4. Prevost's law of heat exchange states that *a body at the same temperature as its surroundings radiates and absorbs heat at the same rates.*

TRUE-FALSE QUESTIONS

T   F   1. The relationships which predict heat transfer are based on empirical observations and depend on ideal conditions.

T   F   2. The quantity of heat transferred through a slab of area 4 ft^2 is greater than the quantity of heat conducted through an area of 8 ft^2, assuming that all other parameters are constant.

T   F   3. When a radiator is used to heat a room, the principal method of heat transfer warming the room is convection.

T   F   4. Air-conditioning outlets in the ceiling are more efficient than those on the floor.

T   F   5. All objects emit electromagnetic radiation, regardless of their temperature or the temperature of their surroundings.

96

T F 6. An object which absorbs a large percentage of incident radiation will be a poor emitter of radiation.

T F 7. Due to a similarity in the definition of heat units, the thermal conductivities are the same numerically in the engineering system and the metric system of units.

T F 8. A body at the same temperature as its surroundings radiates and absorbs heat at the same rate.

T F 9. In a composite wall of two or more different materials, the same number of calories are transferred per unit area per unit time through each material after time is allowed for steady flow to be established.

T F 10. The units of thermal conductivity in the metric system may be written $cal \cdot cm/cm^2 \cdot s \cdot C°$.

MULTIPLE-CHOICE QUESTIONS

1. Which of the following geometries will result in the largest convection coefficient?
   (a) vertical plate
   (b) horizontal plate, facing upward
   (c) diagonal plate
   (d) horizontal plate, facing downward

2. When the temperature of an object is doubled, its rate of radiation is increased by a factor of
   (a) 2   (b) 4   (c) 8   (d) 16

3. The dead air space between the walls of a calorimeter cup and its outside container minimizes heat loss due to
   (a) conduction   (b) convection
   (c) radiation   (d) contamination

4. The rate at which heat flows through a solid plate of some materials does *not* depend on
   (a) temperature difference   (b) the thickness
   (c) specific heat   (d) the area

5. The direction of heat flow is always from
   (a) high temperature to low temperature
   (b) high pressure to low pressure
   (c) high density to low density
   (d) a point of higher emissivity

6. Which of the following does not indicate heat flow as a quantity of heat per unit time?
   (a) $kA \, \Delta t/L$ (b) $hA \, \Delta t$ (c) H (d) $e\sigma T^4$

7. The thermal conductivity of a plate is 0.01 kcal/s·m·C°. The plate is 2 cm thick and has a cross section of 4000 cm². If one side is at 150°C and the other at 50°C, the number of kilocalories transferred every second is approximately
   (a) 10 kcal   (b) 20 kcal   (c) 40 kcal   (d) 80 kcal

8. The convection coefficient for a vertical plate is 12.7 x 10⁻⁴ kcal/s·m²·C° when the difference of temperature between the plate and its surroundings is 810°C. How much heat is transferred by convection from each side of the plate in 1 h if the area is 20 cm²?
   (a) 0.206 cal   (b) 12.4 cal   (c) 741 cal   (d) 8410 cal

9. A body having an emissivity of 0.2 and a surface area of 0.2 m² is heated to a temperature of 727°C. The power radiated from the surface is approximately
   (a) 634 W   (b) 1134 W   (c) 1830 W   (d) 2268 W

10. The units Btu/h·ft²·C° are appropriate for the
    (a) convection coefficient   (b) thermal conductivity
    (c) rate of radiation   (d) emissivity

COMPLETION QUESTIONS

1. Two types of convection which apply to most heating systems are
   _____ convection and _____
   convection.

2. For the common laboratory calorimeter, heat losses due to
   _____ are minimized by a dead air space. The
   rubber ring prevents heat losses by _____, and
   radiation losses are minimized by the _____
   _____.

3. Heat is transferred from the sun to the earth by means of
   _____.

4. The rate at which thermal radiation is emitted from a surface
   varies directly with the _____ power of the
   _____.

5. The _____ of a body is a measure of its ability to
   absorb or emit thermal radiation, and it may vary from a value
   of _____ to a value of _____.

6. The convection coefficient is not a property of the solid or
   fluid but depends primarily on the _____
   of the solid. The convection coefficients for a wall, a floor,
   and a ceiling are largest for the _____ and lowest
   for the _____.

7. The British units commonly used for thermal conductivity are the
   _____ and the metric units are the
   _____.

8. Copper has about twice the thermal conductivity of aluminum, but its specific heat is a little less than half that of aluminum. A rectangular block is made from each material, so that they have identical masses and the same surface area at their bases. Each block is heated to 300°C and placed on top of a large cube of ice. The _____ block will sink deeper into the ice because it has a higher _____. The _____ block will stop sinking first because it has a higher

   _____.

9. The warm air over a burning fire will rise under the influence of _____ currents.

10. On a cold day, a piece of iron feels colder to the touch than a piece of wood at the same temperature because the iron has a higher _____.

ANSWERS TO TRUE-FALSE, MULTIPLE CHOICE, AND COMPLETION QUESTIONS

1.	True	1.	b	1.	natural, forced
2.	False	2.	d	2.	convection, conduction,
3.	True	3.	b		polished aluminum surfaces
4.	True	4.	c	3.	radiation
5.	True	5.	a	4.	fourth, absolute temperature
6.	False	6.	d	5.	emissivity, 0, 1
7.	False	7.	b	6.	geometry, floor, ceiling
8.	True	8.	c	7.	$Btu \cdot in/ft^2 \cdot h \cdot F°$,
9.	True	9.	d		$kcal/m \cdot s \cdot C°$
10.	True	10.	a	8.	aluminum, specific heat,
					copper, thermal conductivity
				9.	convection
				10.	thermal conductivity

CHAPTER 20.   THERMAL PROPERTIES OF MATTER

CONTENTS

OBJECTIVES

You should be able to:

1. Distinguish between an *ideal* gas and a *real* gas, giving reasons why some gases closely approximate the ideal condition.

2. Design an experiment demonstrating the variation in pressure of gas as a function of its volume at constant temperature, establish a relationship between pressure and volume, and explain why your data only approximate this relationship.

3. Demonstrate by example or experiment your understanding of the relationship between the volume of gas and its temperature when the pressure is unaltered.

4. Record the mass m_1 of a gas at a temperature T_1, pressure P_1, and volume V_1 and predict the state of the gas at some later instant when any or all of the parameters are changed.

5. Distinguish by example or discussion between evaporation, boiling, and sublimation as forms of vaporization.

6. Describe an experiment which will measure the vapor pressure of a liquid at a given temperature.

7. Suggest two ways to bring the air in a given room to a saturated condition.

DEFINITIONS

Ideal gas - A gas whose behavior is completely unaffected by cohesive forces or molecular volumes. Such gases obey simple laws and can never be liquefied.

Boyle's law - Provided that the mass and temperature of a sample of gas are maintained constant, the volume of the gas is inversely proportional to its absolute pressure.

Charles' law - Provided that the mass and pressure of a gas sample are kept constant, the volume of the sample is directly proportional to its temperature.

Atomic mass - The atomic mass of an element is the mass of an atom of that element compared with the mass of an atom of carbon taken as 12 atomic mass units.

Molecular mass - The sum of the atomic masses of all the atoms making up a molecule.

Mole - One mole of a substance is the mass in grams equal numerically to the molecular mass of a substance.

Avogadro's number - The number of molecules in 1 mol of any substance.

Critical temperature - That temperature above which a gas will not liquefy, regardless of the amount of pressure applied to it.

Evaporation -Vaporization at the surface of a liquid due to the exodus of the more energetic molecules within the liquid.

Saturated vapor pressure - The additional pressure exerted by vapor molecules on a substance and its surroundings under a condition of saturation.

Boiling - Vaporization within the body of a liquid when its vapor pressure equals the pressure on its surface.

Triple point - The temperature and pressure for which a substance may coexist in its solid, liquid, and vapor phases under a condition of equilibrium.

Absolute humidity - The mass of water vapor per unit volume of air.

Relative humidity - The ratio of the actual vapor pressure in the air to the saturated vapor pressure at that temperature.

Dew point - The temperature to which the air must be cooled, at constant pressure, in order to produce saturation.

PHYSICAL CONCEPTS

1. A useful form of the general gas law which does not involve the use of moles is written on the basis that PV/mT is constant. When a gas in state 1 changes to another state 2, we have

$$\frac{P_1 V_1}{m_1 T_1} = \frac{P_2 V_2}{m_2 T_2}$$

where P = pressure
V = volume
m = mass
T = absolute temperature

When one or more of the above quantities does not change, it is eliminated from the above equation. For example if $m_1 = m_2$ and $T_1 = T_2$, we obtain Boyle's law. If the mass and pressure are constant, we get Charles' law.

$$P_1V_1 = P_2V_2 \quad \text{Boyle's law} \qquad \frac{V_1}{T_1} = \frac{V_2}{T_2} \quad \text{Charles' law}$$

2. When applying the general gas law in any of its forms, it must be remembered that the pressure is *absolute pressure* and the temperature is *absolute temperature*.

   Absolute pressure = gauge pressure + atmospheric pressure

   $$T_K = t_C + 273 \qquad T_R = t_F + 460$$

   For example, a pressure measured in an auto tire is 30 lb/in.^{2} at 37°C. These values must be adjusted before substitution into the gas laws:

   $$P = 30 \text{ lb/in.}^2 + 14.7 \text{ lb/in.}^2 = 44.7 \text{ lb/in.}^2 \quad \text{absolute}$$

   $$T = 37 + 273 = 310 \text{ K}$$

3. A more general form of the gas law is obtained by using the concepts of molecular mass M, and the number of *moles* n for a gas. The number of molecules in 1 mol is Avogadro's number N_A.

   $$N_A = \frac{m}{M} \qquad N_A = 6.023 \times 10^{23} \text{ molecules/mol} \qquad \begin{array}{c}\text{Avogadro's}\\\text{number}\end{array}$$

   The number of moles is found by dividing the mass of a gas (in grams) by its molecular mass M:

   $$n = \frac{m}{M} \qquad \text{number of moles}$$

4. Often it is desired to determine the mass, pressure, volume, or temperature of a gas in a single state. The ideal-gas law uses the molar concept to arrive at a more specific equation:

   $$PV = nRT \qquad R = 0.0821 \text{ liter·atm/mol·K}$$

   It should be noted that use of the constant given above restricts the units of P, V, T, and n to those which are in the constant.

5. The *relative humidity* can be computed from saturated-vapor-pressure tables according to the following definition:

   $$\text{Relative humidity} = \frac{\text{actual vapor pressure}}{\text{saturated vapor pressure}}$$

Remember that the *actual* vapor pressure at a particular temperature is the same as the *saturated* vapor pressure for the dew-point
temperature. Refer to the example in your text.

TRUE-FALSE QUESTIONS

T F 1. Provided that the mass and temperature of an ideal
          gas are maintained constant, the volume of a gas is
          directly proportional to its absolute pressure.

T F 2. If the mass and volume of a gas remain constant, doubling
          the pressure will also double the temperature.

T F 3. The mass of a single molecule of a substance is known as
          its molecular mass.

T F 4. At a temperature of 273 K and a pressure of 1 atm, 1 mol
          of any gas will occupy a volume of 22.4 liters.

T F 5. Only absolute temperatures and absolute pressures can be
          used in applying the general gas laws.

T F 6. If the relative humidities inside the house and outside
          the house are the same, the dew points must also be the
          same.

T F 7. The saturated vapor pressure for a substance is greater
          at higher temperatures.

T F 8. All forms of vaporization are cooling processes.

T F 9. It is possible for ice to be in thermal equilibrium with
          boiling water.

T F 10. The same mass of any ideal gas will occupy the same
          volume at standard temperature and pressure.

MULTIPLE-CHOICE QUESTIONS

1. Boyle's law states that when other parameters are held constant,
   (a) pressure varies directly with the volume
   (b) pressure varies directly with temperature
   (c) pressure varies inversely with volume
   (d) volume varies directly with temperature

2. If the mass and pressure of a gas are held constant while its
   volume doubles, the temperature is changed by a factor of
   (a) ¼   (b) ½   (c) 2   (d) 4

3. The amount of water contained in the air of a given room is most
   accurately described by the
   (a) absolute humidity   (b) relative humidity
   (c) vapor pressure   (d) dew point

4. It is possible for a substance to coexist in all three of its phases in equilibrium when the substance is at its
(a) critical pressure
(b) critical temperature
(c) triple point
(d) dew point

5. At a temperature of 273 K and a pressure of 1 atm, 1 mol of any gas will occupy a volume
(a) of 1 liter
(b) of 22.4 m^3
(c) equal to its molecular mass
(d) of 22.4 liters

6. A weather balloon is filled to a volume of 400 liters at 0°C. What will its volume be at 100°C if the pressure is constant?
(a) 147 liters
(b) 255 liters
(c) 293 liters
(d) 547 liters

7. The molecular mass of oxygen is 32. How many molecules are present in 64 g of oxygen? Avogadro's number is 6.02 x 10^{23}.
(a) 3.012 x 10^{23} molecules
(b) 6.02 x 10^{23} molecules
(c) 12.04 x 10^{23} molecules
(d) 24.092 x 10^{23} molecules

8. How many grams of CO_2 (m = 44 g) will occupy a volume of 2000 liters at a pressure of 3 atm and an absolute temperature of 300 K?
(a) 10,719 g   (b) 512 g   (c) 107 g   (d) 244 g

9. When the air temperature is 26°C and the dew point is 10°C, the relative humidity is
(a) 32 percent
(b) 36.5 percent
(c) 43.2 percent
(d) 54.1 percent

10. A 5000-cm^3 container holds 6 g of gas under a pressure of 2 atm and a temperature of 20°C. When 10 g of the same gas fills a 2500-cm^3 container, the temperature rises to 30°C. The new pressure is
(a) 2.71 atm   (b) 3.3 atm   (c) 6.89 atm   (d) 9.31 atm

COMPLETION QUESTIONS

1. Provided that the _____ and _____ of a sample of gas are maintained constant, the _____ of the gas varies inversely with its absolute pressure. This is known as _____ law.

2. In the ideal gas law, the ratio of _____ to _____ is always equal to a constant R, known as the _____ _____ constant.

3. The temperature above which a gas will not liquefy, regardless of the pressure applied, is called the _____.

4. Three types of vaporization are _____, _____, and _____.

5. The temperature to which air must be cooled at constant pressure in order to produce saturation is called the _____ _____.

6. _____ humidity represents the quantity of water vapor per unit volume. _____ humidity, on the other hand, is a percentage based on the ratio of _____ _____ to _____ _____.

7. A _____ is that quantity of a substance which contains the same number of particles as there are atoms in 12 g of carbon 12.

8. If the _____ and _____ of a gas are held constant, Charles' law states that the _____ of a gas is directly proportional to its _____.

9. A mole of any gas contains _____ molecules This number is referred to as _____.

10. The units for the constant R in the ideal-gas law are _____, as determined from the equation.

ANSWERS TO TRUE-FALSE, MULTIPLE CHOICE, AND COMPLETION QUESTIONS

1. False	1. c	1. mass, temperature, volume, Boyle's
2. True	2. c	2. PV, nT, universal gas
3. False	3. a	3. critical temperature
4. True	4. c	4. evaporation, boiling, sublimation
5. True	5. d	5. dew point
6. False	6. d	6. absolute, relative, actual vapor pressure, saturated vapor pressure
7. True	7. c	7. mole
8. False	8. a	8. mass, pressure, volume, temperature
9. True	9. b	9. 6.023×10^{23}, Avogadro's number
10. False	10. c	10. liter·atm/mol·K

CHAPTER 21. THERMODYNAMICS

CONTENTS

OBJECTIVES

You should be able to:

1. Discuss, in 100 words or less, the distinction between *heat* and *work* as two forms of energy.

2. Give two examples in which the *internal energy* of a system can be changed.

3. State the *first law of thermodynamics* in your own words, give two examples in which the law is demonstrated, and represent the first law mathematically in terms of changes which occur with regard to heat, work, and internal energy.

4. Explain the significance of a P-V diagram in describing a thermo-dynamic process.

5. Define and give an illustrated example of each of the following thermodynamic processes:
(a) *adiabatic*, (b) *isochoric*, and (c) *isothermal*.

6. Discuss, in 200 words or less, the practical significance of the *second law of thermodynamics*.

7. Explain the operation and the limitations on the efficiency of several laboratory heat engines.

8. Predict the efficiency of a heat engine in terms of heat input and heat output or in terms of input and output temperatures.

9. Distinguish between *Carnot efficiency* and *actual efficiency* as they apply to heat engines.

10. Determine the *coefficient of performance* for a refrigerator when the appropriate input and output energies or absolute temperatures are given.

DEFINITIONS

Thermodynamics - The science which treats the transformations of thermal energy into mechanical energy and the reverse process, the conversion of work into heat.

P-V diagram - A graph which plots the change in volume as a function of pressure in a thermodynamic process.

Adiabatic process - A thermodynamic process in which there is no exchange of thermal energy between a system and its surroundings. Work is done at the expense of internal energy.

Isochoric process - A thermodynamic process in which the volume of the system remains constant. All absorbed thermal energy contributes to an increase in internal energy.

Isothermal process - A thermodynamic process in which the temperature of the system remains constant. All absorbed energy contributes to useful work.

Throttling process - A thermodynamic process in which fluid at high pressure seeps adiabatically through a porous wall or narrow opening to a region of low pressure.

The first law of thermodynamics - In any thermodynamic process, the net heat absorbed by a system is equal to the sum of the thermal equivalent of the work done by the system and the change in internal energy of the system.

The second law of thermodynamics - It is impossible to construct an engine which, operating in a full cycle, produces no other effect than the extraction of heat from a reservoir and the performance of an equivalent amount of work.

Carnot cycle - An ideal thermodynamic cycle which represents the maximum possible efficiency. For a Carnot engine, it consists of four stages: isothermal expansion, adiabatic expansion, isothermal compression, and adiabatic compression.

Heat engine - A device which converts thermal energy into mechanical work.

Refrigerator - A device which uses mechanical work to extract heat from one reservoir and exhaust it to another.

Coefficient of performance - A measure of the cooling efficiency of a refrigerator; the ratio of the heat extracted from a cold reservoir to the thermal equivalent of the work supplied to the refrigerator.

PHYSICAL CONCEPTS

1. The *first law of thermodynamics* is a restatement of the conserva-
   tion-of-energy principle. It says that the net heat ΔQ put into
   a system is equal to the net work ΔW done by the system plus the
   net change in internal energy ΔU of the system. Symbolically,

   $$\overline{\Delta Q = \Delta W + \Delta U}\qquad\text{first law of thermodynamics}$$

2. In thermodynamics work ΔW is often done on a gas. In such cases
   the work is often represented in terms of pressure and volume.
   A *P-V* diagram is also useful for measuring ΔW.

   $$\overline{\Delta W = P\ \Delta V}\qquad \Delta W = \text{area under } P\text{-}V \text{ curve}$$

3. Special cases of the first law occur when one of the quantities
   doesn't undergo a change.

   (a) *Adiabatic process:* $\Delta Q = 0$ $\Delta W = -\Delta U$

   (b) *Isochoric process:* $\Delta V = 0$ $\Delta W = 0$ $\Delta Q = \Delta U$

   (c) *Isothermal process:* $\Delta T = 0$ $\Delta U = 0$ $\Delta Q = \Delta W$

4. The *second law of thermodynamics* places restrictions on the
   possibility of satisfying the first. In short, it points out
   that in every process there is some loss of energy due to
   frictional forces or other dissipative forces. A 100 percent
   efficient engine, one which converts all input heat to useful
   output work, is not possible.

5. A heat engine is represented generally by Fig. 21-1. The
   meaning of the symbols used in the equations below can be taken
   from the figure. The work done by the engine is the difference
   between input heat and output heat.

   $$\overline{W = Q_{in} - Q_{out}}\qquad \text{work (kcal or J)}$$

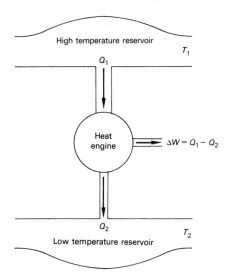

High temperature reservoir

T_1

Q_1

Heat engine

$\Delta W = Q_1 - Q_2$

Q_2

T_2

Low temperature reservoir

Fig. 21-1. A schematic diagram for a heat engine.

The *efficiency* E of an engine is the ratio of the work output to the heat input. It can be calculated for an ideal engine from either of the following relations:

$$E = \frac{Q_{in} - Q_{out}}{Q_{in}} \qquad E = \frac{T_{in} - T_{out}}{T_{in}} \qquad \text{efficiency}$$

6. A *refrigerator* is a heat engine operated in reverse. A measure of the performance of such a device is the amount of cooling you get for the work you must put into the system. Cooling occurs as a result of the extraction of heat Q_{cold} from the cold reservoir. The coefficient of performance η is given by either

$$\eta = \frac{Q_{cold}}{Q_{hot} - Q_{cold}} \qquad \text{or} \qquad \eta = \frac{T_{cold}}{T_{hot} - T_{cold}}$$

TRUE-FALSE QUESTIONS

T F 1. In the absence of friction, heat engines are 100 percent efficient.

T F 2. If the first law óf thermodynamics is satisfied, the second law will also be satisfied.

T F 3. In every thermodynamic process, the heat absorbed by a system must equal the sum of the work done by the system and its change in internal energy.

T F 4. An isochoric process is graphed as a straight line on a P-V diagram.

T F 5. In an adiabatic process, the internal energy will increase when work is done *on* the system whereas it will decrease when work is done *by* the system.

T F 6. During an isothermal expansion, all the absorbed thermal energy is converted into useful work.

T F 7. All Carnot engines are perfect engines and, therefore, operate at 100 percent efficiency.

T F 8. The greater the difference between input and output temperature of a steam engine, the greater the efficiency of the engine.

T F 9. A high compression ratio of an internal combustion engine means a higher operating efficiency.

T F 10. The coefficient of performance for a refrigerator is a measure of cooling efficiency and is expressed as a percent.

MULTIPLE-CHOICE QUESTIONS

1. The thermodynamic state of a gas refers to
   (a) its pressure   (b) its volume
   (b) its temperature   (d) all of these

2. The net work accomplished by an engine undergoing adiabatic compression is equal to
   (a) ΔU (b) $-\Delta U$ (c) ΔQ (d) $-\Delta Q$

3. An engine which operates with 100 percent efficiency
   (a) is a Carnot engine   (b) violates the first law
   (c) has an Otto cycle   (d) violates the second law

4. If a heat engine absorbs heat at 600 K and rejects heat at 200 K, its efficiency is
   (a) 33 percent   (b) 50 percent
   (c) 67 percent   (d) 80 percent

5. In a Carnot cycle, 1600 cal is absorbed at 600 K, and 400 cal is exhausted to a cold reservoir. The temperature of the cold reservoir is
   (a) 150 K   (b) 200 K   (c) 450 K   (d) 800 K

6. An adiabatic process is one in which
   (a) the temperature is constant
   (b) the pressure is constant
   (c) the volume is constant
   (d) no heat enters or leaves the system

7. If the adiabatic constant is 1.4 and the compression ratio is 6, a gasoline engine has an efficiency of
   (a) 45 percent (b) 51 percent
   (c) 56 percent (d) 64 percent

8. In order for a Carnot engine to operate with an efficiency of 100 percent, the exhaust temperature must be
   (a) 0°C (b) 0 K (c) infinite
   (d) equal to the input temperature

9. In a mechanical refrigerator, the low-temperature coils of the evaporator are at -23°C, and the compressed gas in the condenser has a temperature of 77°C. The coefficient of performance is
   (a) 20 percent (b) 70 percent
   (c) 0.23 (d) 2.5

10. In a typical refrigerator, heat is extracted from the interior by the
    (a) compressor (b) evaporator
    (c) condenser (d) throttling valve

COMPLETION QUESTIONS

1. The efficiency of a heat engine is defined as the ratio of the _____ to the _____.

2. An _____ process is one in which the volume remains constant whereas in an _____ process the temperature is constant.

3. The throttling process is an example of an _____ process.

4. The area under the curve on a P-V diagram represents the _____ in a thermodynamic process.

5. Three coordinates used to describe the thermodynamic state of a system are _____, _____, and _____.

6. The _____ is essentially a restatement of the conservation of energy.

7. A _____ is a heat engine operating in reverse. Its effectiveness is measured by the _____ _____.

8. Four essential elements of a typical refrigerator include the _____, the _____, the _____, and the _____.

9. The fact that all natural spontaneous processes are irreversible is a consequence of the _____ _____.

10. A _____ engine has the maximum possible
    efficiency for an engine which absorbs heat from one reservoir,
    performs work, and rejects heat to another reservoir at a lower
    temperature.

ANSWERS TO TRUE-FALSE, MULTIPLE CHOICE, AND COMPLETION QUESTIONS

1.	False	1.	d	1.	work output, work input
2.	False	2.	b	2.	isochoric, isothermal
3.	True	3.	d	3.	adiabatic
4.	True	4.	c	4.	work done on or by the system
5.	True	5.	a	5.	pressure, volume, temperature
6.	True	6.	d	6.	first law of thermodynamics
7.	False	7.	b	7.	refrigerator, coefficient of
8.	True	8.	b		performance
9.	True	9.	d	8.	compressor, condenser
10.	False	10.	b		evaporator, throttling valve
				9.	second law of thermodynamics
				10.	Carnot

CHAPTER 22. WAVE MOTION

CONTENTS

OBJECTIVES

You should be able to:

1. Describe an experiment which demonstrates that energy is associated with wave motion.

2. Define and describe *transverse* and *longitudinal* wave motion using diagrams or actual demonstration.

3. Define, relate, and illustrate the meaning of the terms *frequency*, *speed*, and *wavelength* as they apply to wave motion.

4. Describe the effect of the following parameters on the speed of a mechanical wave: (a) the density of the medium, (b) the elasticity of the medium, (c) the tension in a rope, and (d) the size or shape of a wave.

5. Solve problems involving the mass, length, tension, and wave velocity for transverse waves in a string.

6. Describe how the energy of a given wave depends upon the frequency, amplitude, and medium density.

7. Use the *superposition principle* to determine the resultant waves when two waves of known wavelength and amplitude are given.

8. Write an expression which will predict the characteristic frequencies for a vibrating string with fixed end points.

9. Distinguish between *harmonics* and *overtones* as they apply to a vibrating string with fixed end points.

DEFINITIONS

<u>Wave motion</u> - Energy propagation by means of a disturbance in a medium.

<u>Mechanical wave</u> - A physical disturbance in an elastic medium.

<u>Transverse wave</u> - Wave motion in which the vibration of the individual particles of the medium is perpendicular to the direction of wave propagation.

Longitudinal wave - Wave motion in which the vibration of the individual particles is parallel to the direction of wave propagation.

Wavelength - The distance between any two closest particles along a wave train which are in phase; the distance between adjacent crests in a transverse wave.

Linear density - Mass per unit length, normally used for a string or wire.

Frequency - Number of complete vibrations or oscillations per second.

Wave speed - The distance traveled by a wave pulse per unit of time.

Amplitude - The maximum displacement of a particle in a wave train from its equilibrium position.

Phase - Two particles along a wave train are in phase if they have the same displacement and if they are moving in the same direction.

Superposition principle - When two or more waves exist simultaneously in the same medium, the resultant displacement at any point and time is the algebraic sum of the displacements of each wave.

Constructive interference - The effect of two superimposed waves which result in a wave of larger amplitude than either of the composite waves.

Destructive interference - The effect of two superimposed waves which results in a wave of smaller amplitude than either of the composite waves.

Nodes - Points along a standing wave at which the vibrating medium is not moving.

Antinodes - Points of maximum amplitude along a standing wave.

Standing wave - A wave train for which boundary conditions and frequencies of composite waves result in one or more stationary positions (nodes) along the wave.

Characteristic frequencies - Frequencies of vibration for a given medium under fixed boundary conditions which result in regular standing waves.

Fundamental - The simplest possible standing wave for a given situation which results in the least number of nodal positions.

Overtones - Integral multiples of the fundamental beginning with the next standing wave which occurs after the fundamental.

<u>Harmonics</u> - The entire series of the characteristic frequencies consisting of the fundamental and all its overtones. The first harmonic is the fundamental; the second harmonic is the first overtone; and so on.

PHYSICAL CONCEPTS

1. The velocity of a transverse wave in a string of mass m and length l is given by

$$v = \sqrt{\frac{F}{\mu}} \qquad \mu = \sqrt{\frac{m}{l}} \qquad v = \sqrt{\frac{Fl}{m}} \qquad \text{wave speed}$$

	Force F	mass m	length l	speed v
SI units	N	kg	m	m/s
Bgs units	lb	slug	ft	ft/s

2. For any wave of period T or frequency f, the speed v can be expressed in terms of the wavelength λ as follows:

$$v = \frac{\lambda}{T} \qquad v = f\lambda \qquad \text{frequency is in Hz = 1/s}$$

3. The *energy per unit length* and the *power* of wave propagation can be found from

$$\frac{E}{l} = 2\pi^2 f^2 A^2 \mu \qquad P = 2\pi^2 f^2 A^2 \mu v$$

4. The characteristic frequencies for the possible modes of vibration in a stretched string are found from:

$$f_n = \frac{n}{2l}\sqrt{\frac{F}{\mu}} \qquad n = 1, 2, 3 \ldots \qquad \begin{array}{l}\text{characteristic}\\ \text{frequencies}\end{array}$$

The series $f_n = nf_1$ is called the *harmonics*. They are integral multiples of the fundamental f_1. These are mathematical values and all harmonics may not exist. The actual possibilities beyond the fundamental are called *overtones*. Since all harmonics are possible for the vibrating string, the first overtone is the second harmonic, the second overtone is the third harmonic, and so on.

TRUE-FALSE QUESTIONS

T   F   1. A physical medium is necessary for the transmission of all kinds of waves.

115

T F 2. The speed of a wave in a string is a function of the linear density of the string but is really independent of the actual length of the string.

T F 3. In a longitudinal wave, the wavelength is equal to the distance between adjacent condensations or between adjacent rarefactions.

T F 4. Increasing the frequency of a wave results in a decrease in its wavelength if other parameters are held constant.

T F 5. For a standing wave, the distance between adjacent nodes or between adjacent antinodes is equal to the wavelength.

T F 6. The superposition principle applies only for transverse waves.

T F 7. The third harmonic is equivalent to the second overtone when describing characteristic frequencies.

T F 8. Constructive interference results in a wave of greater energy than the sum of the energies of its component waves.

T F 9. Standing waves are the result of constructive interference.

T F 10. If the frequency of a wave is doubled and other parameters remain the same, the energy of the wave per unit of length will be quadrupled.

MULTIPLE-CHOICE QUESTIONS

1. In a longitudinal wave, the individual particles of the medium move
   (a) in circles
   (b) in elipses
   (c) parallel to wave propagation
   (d) perpendicular to wave propagation

2. For a vibrating string, the third overtone will be the same as the
   (a) second harmonic   (b) third harmonic
   (c) fourth harmonic   (d) fifth harmonic

3. Two particles along a wave train are in phase if they have the same
   (a) displacement   (b) speed
   (c) amplitude   (d) energy

4. A longitudinal wave traveling at 300 m/s has a wavelength of 2 m. Its frequency is
   (a) 100 Hz   (b) 150 Hz   (c) 167 Hz   (d) 600 Hz

5. If 120 waves strike a wall in 1 min and the distance between adjacent crests is 2 m, the speed of the wave is
   (a) 2 m/s   (b) 4 m/s   (c) 8 m/s   (d) 30 m/s

6. A flexible cable 20 m long weighs 16 N and is stretched between two poles with a force of 450 N. The speed of a transverse wave through this medium is
   (a) 16 m/s   (b) 23.7 m/s   (c) 57.3 m/s   (d) 74.2 m/s

7. If the frequency of the fundamental for a vibrating string is 200 Hz, the second overtone has a frequency of
   (a) 200 Hz   (b) 400 Hz   (c) 600 Hz   (d) 800 Hz

8. A metal string of mass 250 g and length 25 cm is under a tension of 400 N. The fundamental frequency for this string is
   (a) 40 Hz   (b) 400 Hz   (c) 126 Hz   (d) 800 Hz

9. The rate at which energy is propagated down a string is not dependent on
   (a) the frequency   (b) the amplitude
   (c) the linear density   (d) the length of the string

10. The ratio of the wavelength to the period is a measure of
    (a) frequency (b) speed   (c) period   (d) amplitude

COMPLETION QUESTIONS

1. In a _____ wave, the vibration of the individual particles is perpendicular to the direction of wave propagation.

2. The speed of a wave in a vibrating string is equal to the square root of the _____ divided by the _____.

3. The distance between any two particles which are in phase is known as the _____.

4. The energy transmitted per unit length of a string is proportional to the square of the _____ and to the square of the _____.

5. For characteristic frequencies of a vibrating string, the fifth harmonic is the _____ overtone.

6. When two or more waves interfere, the resultant _____ at any point and time is the algebraic sum of the _____ of each wave. This is a statement of the _____ principle.

7. For a standing wave, the points along a vibrating string which remain at rest are called _____. The points where the amplitude is a maximum are called _____.

8. The speed of any wave may be found from the product of
_____ and _____.

9. For a standing wave, the wavelength of the component waves is the distance between alternate _____ or between alternate _____.

10. The characteristic frequencies consisting of the fundamental and all its overtones is known as the _____ series.

ANSWERS TO TRUE-FALSE, MULTIPLE CHOICE, AND COMPLETION QUESTIONS

1. False	1. c	1. transverse
2. True	2. c	2. tension, linear density
3. True	3. a	3. wavelength
4. True	4. b	4. frequency, amplitude
5. False	5. b	5. fourth
6. False	6. d	6. displacement, displacements,
7. True	7. c	superposition
8. False	8. a	7. nodes, antinodes
9. True	9. d	8. frequency, wavelength
10. True	10. b	9. nodes, antinodes
		10. harmonic

CHAPTER 23. SOUND

CONTENTS

OBJECTIVES

You should be able to:

1. Distinguish between the physiological and physical definitions of *sound*.

2. Demonstrate by example or experiment your understanding of the production and propagation of a sound wave, including the effects of elasticity and density of a medium.

3. Write an expression for the computation of the speed of sound in a metal rod, in a liquid medium, and in a gas.

4. Compute the approximate speed of sound in air when the temperature is given.

5. Use boundary conditions to derive expressions for computing the characteristic frequencies for an open pipe or for a closed pipe.

6. Give two examples illustrating your understanding of the principle of *resonance*.

7. Relate the physical properties of sound waves to the corresponding sensory effects.

8. Compute the intensity level in *decibels* for a sound whose intensity is given in *watts per square meter*.

9. Discuss the origin and significance of beats.

10. Use your understanding of the Doppler effect to predict the apparent change in sound frequency which occurs as a result of relative motion between a source and an observer.

DEFINITIONS

Sound - A longitudinal mechanical wave which travels through an elastic medium.

Compression - A high-pressure region in a longitudinal wave train where particles are packed tightly together.

Rarefaction - A low-pressure region in a longitudinal wave train where particles are packed tightly together.

Audible sound - Sound waves in the frequency range from 20 to 20,000 Hz, that is, within the range of human hearing.

Infrasonic - Sound waves of frequencies lower than the audible range.

Ultrasonic - Sound waves of frequencies higher than the audible range.

Intensity - The power transferred by a sound wave per unit of area normal to the direction of propagation.

Loudness - A subjective sensory effect which describes human perception of intensity.

Frequency - A physical property of sound which is a measure of the number of longitudinal oscillations per second.

Pitch - A sensory effect which describes human perception of the frequency of a given sound.

Waveform - The complex nature of a sound wave, as might be represented electronically with the use of an oscilloscope (a physical measure of sound quality).

Quality - The sensory effect produced by a sound wave as determined by the number and relative intensities of the overtones which make up the sound.

Forced vibrations - Secondary vibrations set up in an object due to the proximity of a primary vibration.

Resonance - The significant increase in amplitude which occurs whenever a body is acted on by a series of periodic impulses at a frequency equal to one of its natural frequencies of oscillation.

Hearing threshold - The standard zero of sound intensity (10^{-16} W/cm^2).

Pain threshold - The maximum intensity that the average ear can record without a sensation of feeling or pain (the accepted standard is (10^{-4} W/cm^2).

Intensity level - A logarithmic scale of sound intensity which compares the relative intensity of a given sound with that of another sound, usually the hearing threshold. Units are the *bel* and the *decibel*.

Beats - Regular pulsations alternating in intensity due to the interference of two sources of sounds whose frequencies differ only slightly.

Doppler effect - The apparent change in frequency of a source of sound when there is relative motion between the source and the listener.

120

PHYSICAL CONCEPTS

1. Sound is a longitudinal wave traveling through an elastic medium.
   Its speed in air at 0°C is 331 m/s or 1087 ft/s. At other
   temperatures the speed of sound is approximated by

$$v = 331 \text{ m/s} + (0.6 \tfrac{\text{m/s}}{\text{C°}})t_C \qquad \text{speed of sound in air}$$

2. The speed of sound in other media can be found from the following:

$$v = \sqrt{\frac{Y}{\rho}} \quad \text{rod} \qquad\qquad v = \sqrt{\frac{\gamma P}{\rho}} = \sqrt{\frac{\gamma RT}{M}} \quad \text{gas}$$

$$v = \sqrt{\frac{B}{\rho}} \quad \text{fluid} \qquad\qquad v = \frac{\overline{B + (4/3)S}}{\rho} \quad \begin{array}{l}\text{extended} \\ \text{solid}\end{array}$$

3. Standing longitudinal sound waves may be set up in a vibrating air
   column for a pipe that is open at both ends or for one that is
   closed at one end. The characteristic frequencies are

$$f_n = \frac{nv}{2l} \qquad n = 1, 2, 3, \ldots \qquad \text{open pipe of length } l$$

$$f_n = \frac{nv}{4l} \qquad n = 1, 3, 5, \ldots \qquad \text{closed pipe of length } l$$

Note that *only the odd harmonics are possible for a closed pipe.*
In this case, the first overtone is the third harmonic, the second
overtone is the fifth harmonic, and so on.

4. The intensity of a sound is the power P per unit area A perpendicular to the direction of propagation.

$$I = \frac{P}{A} = 2\pi^2 f^2 A^2 \rho v \qquad \text{intensity, W/m}^2$$

5. The intensity level in decibels is given by

$$\beta = 10 \log \frac{I}{I_0} \qquad I_0 = 1 \times 10^{-12} \text{ W/m}^2 \qquad \text{intensity level}$$

6. Whenever two waves are nearly the same frequency and exist
   simultaneously in the same medium, beats are set up such that

Number of beats per second = $f - f'$

7. The general equation for the Doppler effect is

$$f_O = f_s \frac{V + v_O}{V - v_s} \qquad \text{Doppler effect}$$

where f_O = observed frequency
f_s = frequency of source
V = velocity of sound
v_O = velocity of observer
v_s = velocity of source

Note: Speeds are reckoned as positive for approach and negative for recession.

TRUE-FALSE QUESTIONS

T F   1. Sound waves are longitudinal waves which require a medium for transmission.

T F   2. If a tree falls in a forest, there is no sound unless an ear is around to pick up the vibrations.

T F   3. Sound waves travel faster in air than in metals because the air is less dense.

T F   4. The speed of sound is significantly increased with rising temperatures.

T F   5. The quality of different sounds is demonstrated by the difference in tones when a C note is sounded on a flute, a violin, and a trumpet.

T F   6. A sound of intensity level 40 dB is twice as intense as a sound of 20 dB.

T F   7. Sound which fluctuates in intensity due to the simultaneous output of two sources is a consequence primarily of the Doppler effect.

T F   8. In applying Doppler's equation, speeds are reckoned as positive for speeds of approach and negative for speeds of recession.

T F   9. Opening the end of a closed pipe will double the frequency produced.

T F 10. The speed of sound in gases is larger for the gases with higher molecular masses.

MULTIPLE-CHOICE QUESTIONS

1. The speed of sound is greatest when the medium is
   (a) a vacuum   (b) air   (c) water   (d) metal

2. Which of the following is a sensory effect rather than a measurable physical quantity?
   (a) frequency (b) quality   (c) intensity   (d) waveform

3. For a closed pipe, the second overtone is the
   (a) second harmonic   (b) third harmonic
   (c) fourth harmonic   (d) fifth harmonic

4. The physical property which is most responsible for resonance is
   (a) waveform   (b) frequency   (c) quality   (d) intensity

5. Which of the following sounds is loudest?
   (a) 40 dB   (b) 10^{-5} $\mu W/cm^2$ (c) 10^{-10} W/m^2 (d) 3 bels

6. The speed of sound in air at 0°C is 331 m/s. Its speed at 30°C is
   approximately
   (a) 331 m/s   (b) 343 m/s   (c) 349 m/s   (d) 350 m/s

7. The fundamental frequency for a 20-cm closed pipe when the speed
   of sound is 340 m/s is
   (a) 4.25 Hz   (b) 8.25 Hz   (c) 425 Hz   (d) 825 Hz

8. The intensity level in decibels of a sound whose intensity is
   2 x 10^{-6} $\mu W/cm^2$ is approximately
   (a) 27 dB   (b) 43 dB   (c) 50 dB   (d) 103 dB

9. A car horn emits sound at a frequency of 200 Hz. The pitch heard
   when the car is moving at 31 m/s toward an observer in air at 0°C
   is approximately
   (a) 221 Hz   (b) 219 Hz   (c) 181 Hz   (d) 183 Hz

10. Two tuning forks of 340 and 343 Hz are sounded together. The
    resulting beats per second will be
    (a) 1   (b) 2   (c) 3   (d) 4

COMPLETION QUESTIONS

1. The closed end of a pipe must be a displacement _____;
   the open end must be a displacement _____.

2. The velocity of sound waves in a liquid is equal to the square
   root of the ratio of its _____ to its
   _____.

3. The three physical properties of sound which correspond to
   loudness, pitch, and quality are _____, _____,
   and _____, respectively.

4. The _____ represents the standard zero of sound intensity. Its value is _____ W/cm^2.

5. Sound waves having frequencies below the range of audible sound are termed _____; sounds having frequencies above this range are termed _____.

6. For a closed pipe, only the _____ harmonics are possible. Thus, the seventh harmonic will be the _____ overtone.

7. The power transmitted by a sound wave through a unit of area is a measure of _____.

8. The _____ refers to the apparent change in frequency of a source of sound when there is relative motion between the source and the observer. The pitch heard by an observer is _____ when a sound approaches him and _____ when the sound leaves him.

9. Beats are the product of alternating _____ and _____ interference of sound waves of slightly different frequency.

10. When the intensity I_1 of one sound is 10 times as great as the intensity I_2 of another, the difference in intensity levels is said to be 1 _____.

ANSWERS TO TRUE-FALSE, MULTIPLE CHOICE, AND COMPLETION QUESTIONS

1.	True	1.	d	1.	node, antinode
2.	False	2.	b	2.	bulk modulus, density
3.	False	3.	d	3.	intensity, frequency, waveform
4.	True	4.	b	4.	hearing threshold, 10^{-16}
5.	True	5.	c	5.	infrasonic, ultrasonic
6.	False	6.	c	6.	odd, third
7.	False	7.	c	7.	intensity
8.	True	8.	b	8.	Doppler effect, higher, lower
9.	True	9.	d	9.	constructive, destructive
10.	False	10.	c	10.	B

CHAPTER 24.   THE NATURE OF LIGHT

CONTENTS

OBJECTIVES

You should be able to:

1.   Write a one-page report on the history of investigation into the nature of light.

2.   Give an illustration which demonstrates *Huygens' principle* as applied to explain the propagation of light.

3.   State the broad classifications given to electromagnetic radiation in order of increasing wavelength.

4.   Convert *frequency* to *wavelength* and vice versa for an electromagnetic wave.

5.   Write a one-page essay on the contribution of quantum theory to the understanding of the nature of light.

6.   Describe in detail an experiment which would result in a reasonable measurement of the speed of light.

DEFINITIONS

Light - Electromagnetic radiation which is capable of affecting the sense of sight.

Rectilinear propagation - Transmission in a straight line.

Reflection - The property of light which causes it to be turned back into the originating medium when it strikes a smooth surface.

Refraction - The bending of a beam as it passes obliquely from one medium to another.

Huygens' principle - Every point on an advancing wavefront may be considered a source of secondary waves called wavelets; the new position of the wavefront is the envelope of the wavelets emitted from all points of the wavefront in its previous position.

Electromagnetic wave - A wave propagated by oscillating transverse electric and magnetic fields. Oscillations of the electric field are perpendicular to those of the magnetic field, and the collapse of one generates the other in order to sustain the wave without the necessity of a medium. Heat, light, and radio waves are examples.

Electromagnetic spectrum - The entire span of frequencies or wavelengths for all possible electromagnetic waves.

Infrared waves - Electromagnetic radiation which can be broadly classified within the wavelength range between the visible region and the short radio waves (1 to 1000 μm).

Ultraviolet radiation - Electromagnetic radiation of higher frequency or lower wavelength than the visible region but not energetic enough to be classified as x-rays.

Photoelectric effect - The ejection of electrons from a metal plate as a result of an incident beam of light.

Quantum theory - The theory which treats light or other electromagnetic radiation as discrete bundles of energy carried along by a wave field. Such radiation is said to be quantized because only specific energy values are allowed.

PHYSICAL CONCEPTS

1. The wavelength λ of electromagnetic radiation is related to its frequency f by the general equation

$$c = f\lambda \qquad c = 3 \times 10^8 \text{ m/s}$$

2. The range of wavelengths for visible light goes from 400 nm for violet to 700 nm for red.

$$1 \text{ nm} = 10^{-9} \text{ m} \qquad \textit{The nanometer is used for wavelengths.}$$

3. The energy of light photons is proportional to the frequency.

$$E = hf \qquad E = \frac{h\lambda}{c} \qquad h = 6.626 \times 10^{-34} \text{ J/Hz}$$

The constant h is *Planck's constant*.

TRUE-FALSE QUESTIONS

T   F   1. Although earlier scientists believed light was transmitted by particles, it is now established that light is a wave phenomenon.

T   F   2.   Infrared rays are more energetic than visible or ultra-violet rays.

T   F   3.   Interference of light waves is more easily explained on the basis of wave theory of light.

T   F   4.   The propagation of light through outer space is possible due to the presence of a *light-carrying ether*.

T   F   5.   The Michelson-Morley experiment demonstrated that the velocity of light is a constant, independent of the motion of the source.

T   F   6.   The nanometer is 10 times as large as the angstrom.

T   F   7.   The energy of light is directly proportional to the wavelength.

T   F   8.   The first successful terrestrial measurement of the speed of light was made by Fizeau.

T   F   9.   The photoelectric effect occurs when light is emitted as a result of electron bombardment.

T   F   10.   The nature of light is no different fundamentally from the nature of heat radiation.

MULTIPLE-CHOICE QUESTIONS

1. Which of the following is not an electromagnetic phenomenon?
   (a) heat rays   (b) sound waves (c) radio waves   (d) light

2. Which of the following best applies for yellow light?
   (a) 640 nm   (b) 0.4 nm   (c) 5×10^{14} Hz   (d) 580 Å

3. The man most responsible for explaining the photoelectric effect was
   (a) Einstein   (b) Planck   (c) Huygens   (d) Maxwell

4. The wavelength corresponding to light with a frequency of 4×10^{14} Hz is
   (a) 1.33 m   (b) 0.075 μm   (c) 7500 nm   (d) 750 nm

5. A radio frequency of 780 kHz has a wavelength of approximately
   (a) 38 μm   (b) 385 m   (c) 0.0026 m   (d) 26 nm

6. The theory that light is emitted in discrete amounts of energy rather than in a continuous fashion is known as
   (a) the photoelectric effect   (b) the quantum theory
   (c) Huygens' principle   (d) the electromagnetic theory

7. The moon is located approximately 240,000 mi from the earth. A
   radio signal will reach the earth from the moon in
   (a) 1.3 min   (b) 0.775 s   (c) 1.29 s   (d) 0.7 min

8. If Planck's constant is h = 6.625 x 10^{-34} J/Hz, what energy is
   associated with light with a wavelength of 160 nm?
   (a) 1.24 x 10^{-18} J   (b) 1.88 x 10^{15} J
   (c) 1.24 x 10^{-15} J   (d) 1.88 x 10^{-15} J

9. Which of the following scientists measured the speed of light by
   using an eight-sided rotating mirror?
   (a) Fizeau   (b) Roemer   (c) Galileo   (d) Michelson

10. Which of the following terms best describes the nature of light
    from the modern point of view?
    (a) photons   (b) waves   (c) particles   (d) rays

COMPLETION QUESTIONS

1. Every point on an advancing wavefront can be considered as a
   source of secondary _____. This is known as
   _____.

2. The _____ is a unit of wavelength which is equal
   to one ten-thousandth of a micrometer.

3. Electromagnetic radiation of immediately higher energy than light
   is called _____ radiation.

4. Approximate values for the speed of light in a vacuum are
   _____ m/s and _____ mi/s.

5. The conversion factor relating light frequency to light energy is
   known as _____.

6. The common unit for expressing wavelengths of electromagnetic
   radiation is _____.

7. The process by which light is emitted when electrons strike a
   metallic surface is known as the _____.

8. The colors corresponding to the given wavelengths are _____
   (450 nm), _____ (480 nm), _____ (520 nm),
   _____ (580 nm), _____ (600 nm), and _____ (640 nm).

9. The spectrum of electromagnetic waves is divided into the
   following eight major regions in order of increasing energy:
   (a) _____   (b) _____
   (c) _____   (d) _____
   (e) _____   (f) _____
   (g) _____   (h) _____

10. Light energy is equally divided between _____ and
_____ fields which are mutually
perpendicular.

ANSWERS TO TRUE-FALSE, MULTIPLE CHOICE, AND COMPLETION QUESTIONS

1.	False	1.	b	
2.	False	2.	c	
3.	True	3.	a	
4.	False	4.	d	
5.	True	5.	b	
6.	True	6.	b	
7.	False	7.	c	
8.	True	8.	a	
9.	False	9.	d	
10.	True	10.	a	

1. wavelets, Huygens' principle
2. angstrom
3. ultraviolet
4. 3×10^8, 186,000
5. Planck's constant
6. the nanometer
7. photoelectric effect
8. violet, blue, green, yellow, orange, red
9. (a) long radio waves; (b) short radio waves; (c) infrared region; (d) visible region; (e) ultraviolet region; (f) x-rays; (g) gamma rays; (h) cosmic photons.
10. electric, magnetic

CHAPTER 25. LIGHT AND ILLUMINATION

CONTENTS

OBJECTIVES

You should be able to:

1. Illustrate with drawings your understanding of the terms *umbra* and *penumbra*.

2. Explain with drawings *solar* and *lunar eclipses*.

3. Define *luminous flux* and describe a procedure for its measurement.

4. Define *luminous intensity* and describe a procedure for its measurement.

5. Define *illumination* and describe a procedure for its measurement.

6. Explain the significance of a sensitivity curve as a measure of visual response to luminous flux.

7. Record the area of a surface and its distance from a light source and calculate the solid angle in steradians subtended at the source by the surface.

8. Demonstrate by example or experiment your understanding of the inverse-square law as it applies to illumination.

DEFINITIONS

<u>Umbra</u> - The portion of a shadow which receives no light from the source.

<u>Penumbra</u> - The lighter portion of a shadow which receives light from parts of the source but not from all of the source.

<u>Opaque</u> - An object which absorbs and/or reflects all incident light.

<u>Point source</u> - A source of light whose dimensions are very small compared with distances studied.

<u>Light ray</u> - An imaginary line drawn perpendicular to advancing wavefronts which indicates the direction of light propagation.

<u>Luminous flux</u> - That portion of the total radiant power emitted from a light source which is capable of affecting the sense of sight.

Steradian - The solid angle subtended at the center of a sphere by an area A on its surface that is equal to the square of its radius R.

Lumen - The luminous flux emitted from a 1/60-cm^2 opening in a standard source and included within a solid angle of 1 sr. It is also the luminous flux on a unit surface, all points of which are at unit distance from a point source of 1 cd.

Luminous intensity - The luminous flux emitted per unit solid angle for a given light source.

Isotropic source - One which emits light uniformly in all directions, i.e., through a solid angle of 4πsr.

Candela - A unit of measure for luminous intensity which is equal to one lumen per steradian, sometimes referred to as candlepower.

Illumination - The luminous flux per unit area.

PHYSICAL CONCEPTS

1. The *luminous intensity* of a light source is the luminous flux F per unit solid angle Ω. *Luminous flux* is the radiant power in the visible region. It is measured in *lumens*.

$$1 \text{ lm} = \frac{1}{680} \text{ W} \qquad \text{for 555 nm light} \qquad \text{the lumen}$$

$$1 \ \Omega = \frac{A}{R^2} \qquad \text{Solid angle in steradians}$$

$$I = \frac{F}{\Omega} \qquad \text{luminous flux (1 cd = 1 lm/sr)}$$

2. For an isotropic source, one emitting light in all directions, the luminous flux is

$$F = 4\pi I \qquad \text{isotropic source}$$

3. The *illumination* E of a surface A is defined as the luminous flux per unit area.

$$E = \frac{F}{A} \qquad E = \frac{I \cos \theta}{R^2} \qquad \text{illumination, lm/m}^2$$

TRUE-FALSE QUESTIONS

T   F   1. One lumen of red light does not represent the same luminous flux as one lumen of blue light.

T F   2. If a person on the earth sees a quarter moon, he must be within the penumbra of its shadow.

T F   3. If the distance between a surface and a source of light is increased by a factor of 3, the illumination will be one-ninth of its original value.

T F   4. A point source of light will produce only an umbra shadow.

T F   5. Since a candela is equal to a lumen per steradian, the units of intensity and illumination are the same.

T F   6. The luminous intensity is not dependent on the angle a surface makes with incident flux from a source of light.

T F   7. An isotropic source of 1 cd emits a luminous flux of 4π lm.

T F   8. The units of flux and luminous intensity have the same physical dimensions even though they do not represent the same physical quantity.

T F   9. A lumen is the luminous flux falling on 1 m^2 all points of which are located 1 m from a uniform source of 1 cd.

T F 10. The luminous intensity does not change as a surface is moved farther and farther from a light source.

MULTIPLE-CHOICE QUESTIONS

1. Which of the following light sources of equal radiant power appears brightest?
   (a) red light   (b) green light
   (c) blue light   (d) all are the same

2. During a solar eclipse, a person on earth with his eyes protected observes that part of the sun is darkened but never all of it. This person lies in the
   (a) umbra   (b) penumbra
   (c) both (a) and (b)   (d) neither (a) nor (b)

3. What is the luminous flux emitted by a 30-cd isotropic source of light?
   (a) 30 lm   (b) 4 lm   (c) 2.4 lm   (d) 120π lm

4. A 200-cd lamp is 4 m directly above a surface. The illumination is approximately
   (a) 12.5 lm/m^2 (b) 25 lm/m^2 (c) 50 lm/m^2 (d) 80 lm/m^2

5. What angle should a surface make with the incident flux if the illumination of a surface is to be reduced by a factor of one-half?
   (a) 30°   (b) 45°   (c) 60°   (d) 90°

6. A point source of light is placed 20 cm from a pencil 8 cm high. The length of the shadow on a wall 1 m from the source is
   (a) 20 cm   (b) 30 cm   (c) 40 cm   (d) 50 cm

7. The solid angle subtended at the center of a 10-cm-diameter sphere by an area of 2 cm on its surface is approximately
   (a) 0.4 sr   (b) 0.04 sr   (c) 0.8 sr   (d) 0.08 sr

8. Luminous flux is most closely associated with
   (a) the source
   (b) the surface
   (c) the space between the source and the surface
   (d) none of these

9. A movie screen is 10 m from a light source in a projector. The screen makes an angle of 37° with the incident flux. What luminous intensity is required to give an illumination of 6 lm/m^2?
   (a) 75.1 cd   (b) 751 cd   (c) 890 cd   (d) 997 cd

10. A 200-cd light provides an illumination of 50 lm/m^2 at a distance of
   (a) 1 m   (b) 2 m   (c) 3 m   (d) 4 m

COMPLETION QUESTIONS

1. One _____ is equivalent to 1/680 W of yellow-green light of wavelength _____.

2. The inner portion of a shadow which receives no light from the source is called the _____. The other region is known as the _____.

3. The luminous flux per unit solid angle is known as the _____ and is measured in _____.

4. The illumination may be calculated from the ratio of _____ _____ to _____ or from the ratio of _____ _____ to the square of the _____ between the source and the surface.

5. A grease-spot photometer is used to measure _____ by comparison with a standard source.

6. A _____ is the solid angle subtended at the center of a sphere by an area on its surface that is equal to the square of its _____.

7. The _____ of a surface is proportional to the luminous intensity of the light source and is inversely proportional to the square of the distance. This is sometimes called the _____ law.

8. When a surface makes an angle with the incident flux, the _____ is proportional to the component of the surface _____ to the flux.

9. An _____ source is one which emits light uniformly in all directions.

10. The _____ is that part of the total radiant power emitted from a light source which is capable of affecting the sense of sight.

ANSWERS TO TRUE-FALSE, MULTIPLE CHOICE, AND COMPLETION QUESTIONS

1. False	1. b	1. lumen, 555 nm
2. False	2. b	2. umbra, penumbra
3. True	3. d	3. luminous intensity, candelas
4. True	4. a	4. flux, area, luminous intensity, distance
5. False	5. c	
6. True	6. c	5. intensity
7. True	7. d	6. steradian, radius
8. True	8. c	7. illumination, inverse-square
9. True	9. d	8. illumination, perpendicular
10. True	10. b	9. isotropic
		10. luminous flux

CHAPTER 26. REFLECTION AND MIRRORS

CONTENTS

OBJECTIVES

You should be able to:

1. Distinguish between *specular* and *diffuse reflection*.

2. Write and demonstrate two laws that pertain to the reflection of light.

3. Demonstrate with drawings your understanding of the nature of images formed by plane mirrors.

4. Demonstrate by definition and by experiment your understanding of the distinction between *virtual* and *real* images.

5. State at least two practical uses for, or advantages of, concave mirrors.

6. State at least two practical uses for, or advantages of, convex mirrors.

7. Use ray-tracing techniques to construct images formed by spherical mirrors.

8. Predict mathematically the nature, size, and location of images formed by spherical mirrors.

9. Define *magnification* and describe a procedure for its measurement.

10. Define the *focal length* of a spherical mirror and calculate the focal length both mathematically and experimentally.

11. Discuss the effects of spherical aberration on the formation of images and suggest a means of preventing or reducing this undesirable phenomenon.

DEFINITIONS

Reflection - The process by which incident light is turned back into its original medium upon striking a surface.

Specular reflection - Regular reflection in which incident parallel rays of light remain parallel after reflection.

Diffuse reflection - Irregular reflection in which incident light is scattered as it strikes a rough surface.

Mirror - A highly polished surface which forms images by specular reflection of light.

Virtual image - An image which seems to be formed by light coming from it although no light rays actually pass through it.

Real image - An image formed by actual light rays which pass through it. Real images can be projected on a screen.

Concave spherical mirror - A spherical mirror in which the reflecting surface is curved inward.

Convex spherical mirror - A spherical mirror in which the reflecting surface is curved outward.

Diverging mirror - A mirror on which incident light will diverge after reflection.

Converging mirror - A mirror which converges light after reflection.

Center of curvature - The center of the imaginary sphere which would be formed if the surface of a spherical mirror were fully extended.

Vertex - The topographical center of the reflecting surface on a mirror.

Focal point, or focus - The point to which parallel light rays converge or from which they appear to diverge after reflection.

Focal length - The distance from the vertex of a mirror to its focal point.

Radius of curvature - The radius of an imaginary sphere constructed by fully extending the surface of a spherical mirror.

Magnification - The ratio of the image size to the object size for images formed by mirrors.

Spherical aberration - The focusing defect of a spherical mirror in which the extreme rays of light are not sharply focused.

PHYSICAL CONCEPTS

1. The formation of images by spherical mirrors can be visualized more easily with ray-tracing techniques. The three rays are shown in Fig. 26-1 for converging and diverging mirrors.

Ray 1.   A ray parallel to the mirror axis passes through the focal point of a concave mirror or seems to come from the focal point of a convex mirror.

Ray 2.   A ray that passes through the focal point of a concave mirror or proceeds toward the focal point of a convex mirror is reflected parallel to the mirror axis.

Ray 3.   A ray which proceeds along a radius of the mirror is reflected back along its original path.

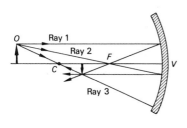 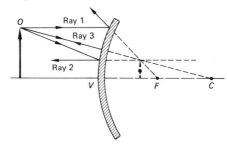

(a)   (b)

Fig. 26-1.   (a) Ray tracing for a converging mirror; (b) Ray tracing for a diverging mirror.

2.   Before listing the mirror equations, you should review what the symbols mean and the sign conventions.

R = radius of curvature   + for converging, - for diverging
f = focal length   + for converging, - for diverging
p = object distance   + for real object, - for virtual
q = image distance   + for real images, - for virtual
y = object size   + if erect, - if inverted
y'= image size   + if erect, - if inverted
M = magnification   + if both erect or both inverted

3.   The mirror equations can be applied to either converging (concave) or diverging (convex) spherical mirrors:

$$f = \frac{R}{2} \qquad R = 2f \qquad M = \frac{y'}{y} \qquad \frac{1}{p} + \frac{1}{q} = \frac{1}{f} \qquad \text{mirror equations}$$

Alternate forms for the last equation are:

$$p = \frac{qf}{q - f} \qquad q = \frac{pf}{p - f} \qquad f = \frac{pq}{p + q}$$

TRUE-FALSE QUESTIONS

T   F   1.   A negative magnification results whenever the image is virtual.

T F 2. A virtual image cannot be formed on a screen.

T F 3. Images formed by convex spherical mirrors are always virtual, erect, and enlarged.

T F 4. For concave spherical mirrors, the magnification is always greater than one when the object is located between the center of curvature and the focal point.

T F 5. A plane mirror forms real images.

T F 6. Objects moving closer and closer to the vertex of a convex mirror form smaller and smaller images.

T F 7. In a concave shaving mirror, greater magnification is achieved when the object is closer to the focal point.

T F 8. All virtual images formed by spherical mirrors are erect and diminished.

T F 9. A ray parallel to the mirror axis passes through the center of curvature after reflection from a converging mirror.

T F 10. The radius of curvature is equal to twice the focal length for both concave and convex mirrors.

MULTIPLE-CHOICE QUESTIONS

1. For a spherical concave mirror, virtual images are formed when the object is located
   (a) between F and C (b) beyond C
   (c) at C (d) inside F

2. Which of the following is *not* true when an image is formed by an object located between C and F of a concave mirror?
   (a) negative magnification   (b) negative image distance
   (c) inverted image   (d) enlarged image

3. The focal point of a convex spherical mirror is
   (a) twice the radius   (b) in front of the mirror
   (c) virtual   (d) real

4. Which of the following is *not* true for images formed by a plane mirror?
   (a) magnification is +1   (b) image distance is negative
   (c) right and left are reversed (d) images are real

5. A source of light 12 cm high is placed 50 cm from a concave mirror of focal length 100 cm. The image distance is
   (a) -100 cm   (b) +100 cm   (c) +50 cm   (d) -50 cm

6. An object is placed 10 cm from the vertex of a convex spherical mirror whose radius is 20 cm. The magnification is
(a) 0.667   (b) -0.667   (c) +½   (d) -½

7. A 6-ft man stands 20 ft from a plane mirror. The shortest mirror required to view the entire image is
(a) 3 ft   (b) 6 ft   (c) 9 ft   (d) 12 ft

8. Where must an object be placed in order to form an image on a screen 30 cm from the vertex of a mirror whose radius is 20 cm?
(a) 20 cm   (b) 15 cm   (c) 10 cm   (d) 5 cm

9. The magnification of a mirror is -1/3. What is the image distance when an object is placed 24 cm from this mirror?
(a) 8 cm   (b) -8 cm   (c) 12 cm   (d) -12 cm

10. What should be the object distance for a concave shaving mirror of radius 3.2 m in order to form an erect image twice as large as the object?
(a) 80 cm   (b) 1.6 m   (c) 2.4 m   (d) 3.2 m

COMPLETION QUESTIONS

1. The focal length of a spherical mirror is equal to _____
_____ .

2. All images formed by convex mirrors are _____ , _____ , and _____ in size.

3. Object and image distances must be reckoned as _____ for real objects or images and _____ for virtual ones.

4. A magnification less than 0 but greater than -1 means that the image is _____ than the object in size and is also _____ .

5. When an object is placed inside the focus of a concave mirror, the image is _____ , _____ , and _____ in size.

6. The magnification is equal to the ratio of the _____ to the _____ and will be _____ for erect images and _____ for inverted images.

7. When an object is located at the focal point of a concave mirror, all reflected rays are_____ .

8. A ray which proceeds toward the focal point of a concave mirror, is reflected_____ .

9. A _____ image appears to be formed by actual rays of light, but no rays of light actually pass through it.

139

10. The linear apertures of spherical mirrors should be _____ in comparison with their focal lengths in order to reduce the effects of _____.

ANSWERS TO TRUE-FALSE, MULTIPLE CHOICE, AND COMPLETION QUESTIONS

1.	False	1.	d	1.	one-half the radius of curvature
2.	True	2.	b	2.	virtual, erect, diminished
3.	False	3.	c	3.	positive, negative
4.	True	4.	d	4.	smaller, inverted
5.	False	5.	a	5.	virtual, erect, enlarged
6.	False	6.	c	6.	image size, object size, positive, negative
7.	True	7.	a	7.	parallel
8.	True	8.	b	8.	parallel to the mirror axis
9.	False	9.	a	9.	virtual
10.	True	10.	a	10.	small, spherical aberration

CHAPTER 27.   REFRACTION

CONTENTS

OBJECTIVES

You should be able to:

1. Define the *index of refraction* and suggest a procedure for its measurement.

2. Write and illustrate with drawings three laws which can be applied to explain the phenomenon of refraction.

3. Apply Snell's law to the solution of problems involving light transmission in two or more media.

4. Predict mathematically the change in wavelength which occurs when light travels from one medium to another.

5. Define and demonstrate the phenomenon of *dispersion*.

6. Give at least two examples to illustrate your understanding of *total internal reflection*.

7. Compute the *critical angle* for a known material, both mathematically and experimentally.

8. Apply Snell's law to relate the *apparent* depth of a submerged object to its *actual* depth.

DEFINITIONS

Refraction - The bending of a light ray as it passes obliquely from one medium to another.

Index of refraction - The ratio of the free-space velocity of light to the velocity of light through a specific material.

Optical density - A property of a material which is a measure of the speed of light through it. This term is sometimes used instead of the refractive index.

Snell's law - The ratio of the sine of the angle of incidence to the sine of the angle of refraction is equal to the ratio of the velocity of light in the incident medium to the velocity of light in the refracted medium.

<u>Dispersion</u> - The separation of light into its component wavelengths, usually accomplished with a prism.

<u>Critical angle</u> - The limiting angle of incidence in a denser medium, which results in an angle of refraction equal to 90°.

<u>Total internal reflection</u> - The process by which light incident from a denser medium is reflected back into that medium upon striking the boundary between two media.

PHYSICAL CONCEPTS

1. The index of refraction of a particular material is the ratio of the free-space velocity of light c to the velocity v of light through the medium.

$$n = \frac{c}{v} \qquad c = 3 \times 10^8 \text{ m/s} \qquad \text{index of refraction}$$

2. When light enters from medium 1 and is refracted into medium 2, Snell's law can be written in the following two forms (see Fig. 27-1):

$$n_1 \sin \theta_1 = n_2 \sin \theta_2 \qquad \frac{v_1}{v_2} = \frac{\sin \theta_1}{\sin \theta_2} \qquad \text{Snell's law}$$

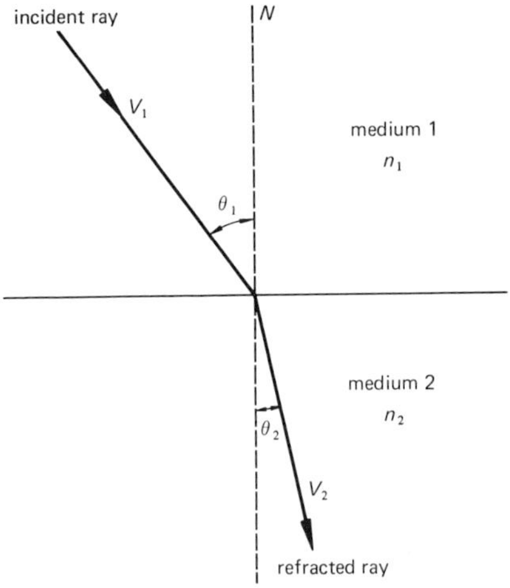

incident ray $\quad$ N

V_1

medium 1
n_1

θ_1

medium 2
n_2

θ_2

V_2

refracted ray

Fig. 27-1. Snell's law.

3. When light enters medium 2 from medium 1, its wavelength is changed by the fact that the index of refraction is different.

$$\frac{\lambda_1}{\lambda_2} = \frac{n_2}{n_1} \qquad \lambda_2 = \frac{n_1 \lambda_1}{n_2}$$

142

4. The critical angle θ_c is the maximum angle of incidence from one medium which will still produce refraction (at 90°) into a bordering medium. From the definition, we obtain

$$\sin \theta_c = \frac{n_2}{n_1} \qquad \text{critical angle}$$

5. Refraction causes an object in one medium to be observed at a different depth when viewed from above in another medium.

$$\frac{\text{Apparent depth } q}{\text{Actual depth } p} = \frac{n_2}{n_1}$$

TRUE-FALSE QUESTIONS

T F 1. When light enters from a medium of lower refractive index into a medium of larger refractive index, the path of the light bends toward the normal.

T F 2. When light crosses a boundary between medium 1 and medium 2, the ratio of v_1 to v_2 will be the same as the ratio of n_1 to n_2.

T F 3. Objects of higher optical density have greater critical angles.

T F 4. When white light is dispersed by a prism, the smaller-wavelength components are deviated the most.

T F 5. For total internal reflection, the angle of incidence is equal to the angle of reflection.

T F 6. When an object in air is viewed from a position under water, the object appears to be farther away than it actually is.

T F 7. Whenever light enters a denser medium, both the velocity and frequency of the light are reduced.

T F 8. Whenever light passes through any number of parallel media and finally returns to the original medium, the angle of incidence in the original medium is equal to the angle of emergence.

T F 9. The critical angle for right-angle prisms should not exceed 45°.

T F 10. The lateral displacement of light as it passes through a pane of glass is greater when the optical density of the glass is large.

MULTIPLE-CHOICE QUESTIONS

1. For refraction of light from medium 1 to medium 2, the ratio of $\sin \theta_1$ to $\sin \theta_2$ is equal to
   (a) v_1/v_2　　　(b) n_1/n_2　　　(c) x_2/x_1　　　(d) θ_1/θ_2

2. The index of refraction for a substance is
   (a) constant
   (b) constant for a given wavelength
   (c) variable with the speed of light
   (d) never constant

3. Total internal reflection occurs when the angle of incidence is
   (a) greater than the angle of refraction
   (b) equal to the critical angle
   (c) greater than the critical angle
   (d) greater than 45°

4. The refractive index of benzene is 1.5.　The velocity of light in benzene is approximately
   (a) 1.5×10^8 m/s　　　　　(b) 1.75×10^8 m/s
   (c) 2×10^8 m/s　　　　　(d) 2.5×10^8 m/s

5. Light passes at an angle of incidence of 37° from water to air. The angle of refraction in the air is approximately
   (a) 27°　　　(b) 53°　　　(c) 45°　　　(d) 60°

6. Monochromatic green light has a wavelength of 520 nm.　The wavelength of this light inside glass of refractive index 1.5 is approximately
   (a) 300 m　　　(b) 340 m　　　(c) 520 m　　　(d) 780 m

7. The critical angle for diamond (n = 2.42) surrounded by air is approximately
   (a) 24°　　　(b) 35°　　　(c) 45°　　　(d) 66°

8. A fish is located 2 m from the surface of a small pond.　His apparent depth is
   (a) 1.0 m　　　(b) 1.5 m　　　(c) 2.0 m　　　(d) 2.66 m

9. Light is incident from water at an angle of 60° into a transparent medium.　If the angle of refraction is 30°, the index for the medium is
   (a) 1.15　　　(b) 1.5　　　(c) 2.3　　　(d) 3.1

10. Light travels from air at an angle of incidence of 41°.　What will the speed of light in the second medium be if the angle of refraction is 30°?
    (a) 1.5×10^8 m/s　　　　　(b) 2.1×10^8 m/s
    (c) 2.29×10^8 m/s　　　　　(d) 2.5×10^8 m/s

COMPLETION QUESTIONS

1. The _____ of a material is the ratio
   of the free-space velocity of light to the velocity of light
   through the material.

2. For refraction the _____, the _____
   _____, and the _____ all lie in
   the same plane.

3. Whenever light enters glass from air, the _____
   remains unchanged, but the _____ and the
   _____ are reduced.

4. Whenever white light enters a prism, it separates into its
   component _____. This phenomenon is known as
   _____.

5. The _____ is the limiting angle of
   incidence in a denser medium which results in an angle of
   refraction of 90°.

6. Total internal reflection occurs when a light ray from a certain
   medium is incident upon another medium of _____ optical
   density at an angle of incidence greater than the
   _____.

7. According to Snell's law, the ratio of the _____
   _____ to the _____
   _____ is equal to the ratio of the _____
   _____ in the incident medium to the _____
   _____ in the refracted medium.

8. Right-angle prisms make use of the principle of _____
   _____ to deviate the path of
   light along right angles.

9. When objects under water are viewed from the air above the water,
   the apparent depth is equal to the actual depth times the ratio
   of _____ _____ to
   the _____.

10. The minimum value of the index of refraction is _____.

ANSWERS TO TRUE-FALSE, MULTIPLE CHOICE, AND COMPLETION QUESTIONS

1.	True	1.	a	1.	index of refraction
2.	False	2.	b	2.	incident ray, refracted ray,
3.	False	3.	c		normal to the surface
4.	True	4.	c	3.	frequency, wavelength, velocity
5.	True	5.	b	4.	wavelengths, dispersion
6.	True	6.	b	5.	critical angle
7.	False	7.	a	6.	lower, critical angle

145

ANSWERS (Continued)

8. True   8. b   7. sine of the angle of incidence,
9. True   9. c   sine of the angle of refrac-
10. True   10. c   tion, velocity of light,
                                 velocity of light
                             8. total internal reflection
                             9. the index of refraction in air,
                                 index of refraction in water
                             10. 1

CHAPTER 28. LENSES AND OPTICAL INSTRUMENTS

CONTENTS

OBJECTIVES

You should be able to:

1. Demonstrate the distinction between *converging* and *diverging* *lenses*, either graphically or experimentally.

2. Determine the focal lengths of an assortment of spherical lenses and state whether they are converging or diverging lenses.

3. Apply the *lensmaker's equation* to solve for unknown parameters related to the construction of lenses.

4. Use ray-tracing techniques to construct images formed by diverging and converging lenses for various object locations.

5. Predict mathematically or determine experimentally the nature, size, and location of images formed by converging and diverging lenses.

6. Design an experiment which would determine the magnification of a given lens for a given object distance.

7. Explain with diagrams the operation of a microscope, a telescope, a simple camera, or a projector.

8. Determine the focal length of a lens mathematically when the necessary information is given.

9. Discuss the effects of *spherical aberration* and *chromatic aberration* as they apply to the formation of images by lenses and suggest a procedure for correcting or reducing these effects.

DEFINITIONS

Lens - A transparent object which alters the shape of a wavefront that passes through it.

Converging lens - A lens which refracts and converges parallel light to a point focus beyond the lens.

Diverging lens - A lens which refracts and diverges parallel light from a point located in front of the lens.

Focal length - The distance from the optical center of a lens to either focus.

Lensmaker's equation - The physical relationship between the focal length, surface curvatures, and refractive index that guides in the construction of lenses.

Magnification - The ratio of image size to object size for images formed by lenses.

Compound microscope - An optical instrument consisting of two converging lenses arranged to achieve large magnification of small objects at close range.

Telescope - An optical instrument designed to examine large distant objects.

Objective lens - The outermost lens of an optical instrument which first receives light from the object being viewed.

Eyepiece - The lens of an optical instrument through which light leaves the instrument and enters the eye.

Spherical aberration - A lens defect in which the extreme rays are brought to a focus nearer the lens than those rays entering near the optical center of the lens.

Chromatic aberration - A lens defect which reflects its inability to focus light of different colors (wavelengths) to the same point.

PHYSICAL CONCEPTS

1. Image formation by thin lenses can be understood more easily through ray-tracing techniques as illustrated in Fig. 28-1. Remember that the first focal point F_1 is the one on the same side of the lens as the incident light. The second focal point F_2 is on the far side.

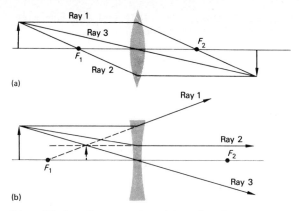

(a)

(b)

Fig. 28-1. Ray construction for lenses.

Ray 1. *A ray parallel to the axis passes through the second*
focal point F_2 of a converging lens or appears to come
from the first focal point F_1 of a diverging lens.

Ray 2. *A ray that passes through F_1 of a converging lens or*
proceeds toward F_2 of a diverging lens is refracted
parallel to the lens axis.

Ray 3. *A ray which passes through the geometrical center of*
a lens will not be deviated.

2. The *lensmaker's equation* is a relationship between the focal
length, the radii of the two lens surfaces, and the index of
refraction of the lens material. The meaning of these parameters
is seen from Fig. 28-2.

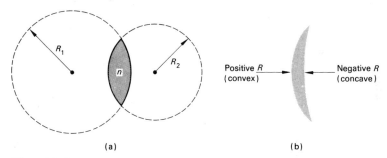

(a)   (b)

Fig. 28-2.

$$\frac{1}{f} = (n - 1) \left(\frac{1}{R_1} + \frac{1}{R_2}\right) \qquad \text{lensmaker's equation}$$

R_1 or R_2 is + if outside surface is convex, − if concave.

f is considered + for converging lens and − for diverging.

3. The equations for object and image locations and for the magnification are the same as for the mirror equations.

$$\frac{1}{p} + \frac{1}{q} = \frac{1}{f} \qquad p = \frac{qf}{q - f} \qquad q = \frac{pf}{p - f} \qquad f = \frac{pq}{p + q}$$

$$Magnification = \frac{image\ size}{object\ size} \qquad M = \frac{y'}{y} = \frac{-q}{p}$$

P or q is + for real and - for virtual

y or y' is + if erect and - if inverted

TRUE-FALSE QUESTIONS

T F 1. A lens which is thinner in the middle than it is at the the edges will be a converging lens.

T F 2. A plano-concave lens has a virtual focus.

T F 3. Both surfaces of a converging meniscus lens should be reckoned as positive, according to convention.

T F 4. Virtual images are formed on the same side of the lens as the object.

T F 5. The overall magnification of a compound optical instrument is equal to the product of the magnifications of the component lenses.

T F 6. Chromatic aberration is a lens defect in which the extreme rays are brought to a focus nearer the lens than those rays entering near the optical center of the lens.

T F 7. According to convention, the object distance is reckoned as negative when measured to a virtual object.

T F 8. All images formed by diverging lenses are virtual, diminished, and erect.

T F 9. In a simple microscope, the greatest magnification occurs as the object gets closer and closer to the lens surface.

T F 10. Whenever the object is beyond the focal point of a converging lens, the magnification will always be negative.

MULTIPLE-CHOICE QUESTIONS

1. Images formed from real objects by diverging lenses are always
   (a) virtual   (b) enlarged   (c) inverted   (d) real

2. A diverging lens may not have
   (a) a negative focal length   (b) a positive focal length
   (c) one plane surface   (d) one convex surface

3. For a compound microscope, the image formed by the eyepiece is
   (a) real   (b) inverted   (c) erect   (d) diminished

4. A negative magnification always means that the image is
   (a) erect   (b) real   (c) virtual   (d) inverted

5. Which of the following is *not* true for images formed by real
   objects located inside the focal point of a converging lens?
   (a) virtual   (b) erect   (c) real   (d) enlarged

6. A meniscus lens has a convex surface of curvature 20 cm and a
   concave surface of curvature -30 cm. If the lens is constructed
   from glass (n = 1.5), the focal length will be
   (a) -4 cm   (b) +4 cm   (c) -120 cm   (d) +120 cm

7. An object is located 10 in. from a thin converging lens whose
   focal length is 30 in. The image distance is approximately
   (a) -7.5 in.   (b) +7.5 in.   (c) 15 in.   (d) -15 in.

8. A diverging meniscus lens has a focal length of -20 cm. If the
   lens is held 10 cm from the object, the magnification is
   (a) -0.667   (b) +0.667   (c) -2   (d) +2

9. A plano-convex lens is ground from glass (n = 1.5). If the
   focal length is to be 20 cm, the radius of the curved surface
   should be
   (a) 10 cm   (b) 20 cm   (c) 30 cm   (d) 40 cm

10. A 6-ft high image is projected on a screen located 40 ft from
    a converging lens. If the object size is 0.2 ft, the focal
    length must be
    (a) 0.736 ft   (b) 1.29 ft   (c) 1.38 ft   (d) 2.79 ft

COMPLETION QUESTIONS

1. Images formed by diverging lenses are always _____,
   _____, and _____ in size.

2. The _____ of a lens is the dis-
   tance from the optical center of the lens to either focus.

3. An object at a distance beyond twice the focal length of a convex
   lens forms an image that is _____, _____,
   and _____ in size.

4. The object distance and the image distance are considered
_____ for real images and objects and
_____ for virtual images and objects.

5. A positive magnification means that the image is _____,
and a negative magnification means the image is _____.

6. Three examples of converging lenses are _____,
_____, and _____.

7. A converging lens is _____ in the middle than at
the edges whereas a diverging lens is _____ in the
middle.

8. A ray parallel to the axis passes through the _____
_____ of a converging lens or appears to
come from the _____ of a
diverging lens.

9. A _____ image is formed on the same side of the lens
as the object; a _____ image is formed on the opposite
side.

10. A ray which passes through the _____ of a lens will
not be deviated.

ANSWERS TO TRUE-FALSE, MULTIPLE CHOICE, AND COMPLETION QUESTIONS

1.	False	1.	a	1.	virtual, erect, diminished
2.	True	2.	b	2.	focal length
3.	False	3.	b	3.	real, inverted, diminished
4.	True	4.	d	4.	positive, negative
5.	True	5.	c	5.	erect, inverted
6.	False	6.	d	6.	double convex, plano-convex,
7.	True	7.	d		converging meniscus
8.	True	8.	b	7.	thicker, thinner
9.	False	9.	a	8.	second focal point, first
10.	True	10.	b		focal point
				9.	virtual, real
				10.	center

CHAPTER 29. INTERFERENCE, DIFFRACTION, AND POLARIZATION

CONTENTS

OBJECTIVES

You should be able to:

1. Explain why the phenomena of diffraction and interference demonstrate the wave nature of light.

2. Give graphic examples to illustrate your understanding of *constructive* and *destructive interference*.

3. Become familiar with Young's experiment to the extent that you are able to predict the location of bright and dark fringes.

4. Set up a crude model of Young's experiment in the laboratory in order to determine the wavelength of a given source of mono- chromatic light experimentally.

5. Derive the *grating equation*.

6. Determine the wavelength of the blue and green interference fringes from a mercury arc lamp when a diffraction grating and an optical bench with accessories are provided.

7. Apply the grating equation to the solution of problems involving the use of diffraction gratings.

8. Discuss the meaning and practical significance of *resolving power* as it relates to optical instruments.

9. Define and demonstrate the phenomenon of *polarization*.

DEFINITIONS

Diffraction - The ability of waves to bend around obstacles placed in their path.

Constructive interference - The process by which two or more waves interact to result in a composite wave of greater amplitude than the component waves.

Destructive interference - Interference which results in a composite wave of smaller amplitude than the component waves.

Young's experiment - A classic experiment which predicts the location
   of interference fringes produced by passing monochromatic light
   through two slits.

Diffraction grating - An optical device consisting of many parallel
   slits which produce a spectrum through the interference of light
   diffracted through them.

Order - A system of numbering interference fringes as they move away
   from the central fringe.

Resolving power - A measure of the ability of an instrument to
   produce well-defined separate images.

Polarization - The process by which the oscillations of wave motion
   are confined to a definite pattern.

Plane polarization - Polarization in which the oscillations are
   restricted to a plane.

PHYSICAL CONCEPTS

1. In Young's experiment interference and diffraction account for
    the production of bright and dark fringes. The location of
    these fringes is given by the following equations (see Fig. 29-1):

$$\text{Bright fringes:} \quad \frac{yd}{x} = n\lambda \qquad n = 0, 1, 2, 3, \ldots$$

$$\text{Dark fringes:} \quad \frac{yd}{x} = n\lambda \qquad n = 1, 3, 5, 7, \ldots$$

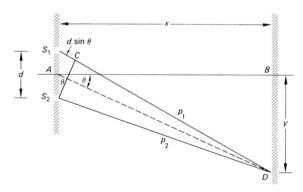

Fig. 29-1.

2. In a diffraction grating of slit separation d, the wavelengths of
    the nth order fringes are given by

$$d \sin \theta_n = n\lambda \qquad n = 1, 2, 3, \ldots$$

3. The resolving power of an instrument is a measure of its ability to produce well-defined separate images. The minimum conditions for resolution are illustrated in Fig. 29-2. For this situation the resolution equation is

$$\theta_0 = 1.22\frac{\lambda}{D} = \frac{s_0}{p} \qquad \text{resolving power}$$

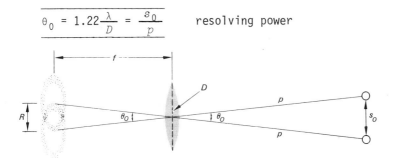

Fig. 29-2. Resolution of two distant objects by a spherical lens.

TRUE-FALSE QUESTIONS

T   F   1.   In an interference pattern, the bright lines are due to constructive interference, and the dark lines are caused by destructive interference.

T   F   2.   A diffraction grating deviates red light more than blue light.

T   F   3.   In Young's experiment, decreasing the separation of the two slits will also decrease the separation of the interference fringes.

T   F   4.   The resolving power of a telescope depends on the diameter of its objective lens and is not a function of the magnification.

T   F   5.   First-order images are bright lines, and second-order images are dark lines.

T   F   6.   The limit of resolution for two objects occurs when the central maximum of the interference pattern of one object coincides with the first dark fringe of the interference pattern from the other object.

T   F   7.   Both transverse and longitudinal waves can be polarized by an appropriate choice of material to serve as a polarizer.

T   F   8.   The angular separation θ_0 of two distant objects at the limit of resolution is a more accurate measure of resolving power than their linear separation d_0.

T   F   9.   The greater the number of lines per inch on a diffraction grating, the greater the angle of deviation for the diffracted light.

T   F   10. A polarizer can also be used as an analyzer in studying polarized light.

MULTIPLE-CHOICE QUESTIONS

1. The resolving power of an instrument is determined by the
   (a) magnification
   (b) focal length of the objective lens
   (c) diameter of the objective lens
   (d) none of these

2. The main advantage of a grating over Young's apparatus is the
   (a) sharpness of the bright lines
   (b) absence of dark fringes
   (c) absence of bright fringes
   (d) greater deviation of light

3. Which of the following demonstrates the transverse nature of light waves?
   (a) interference   (b) polarization
   (c) diffraction   (d) refraction

4. The wavelength of light from a distant object does not affect
   (a) interference   (b) resolving power
   (c) diffraction   (d) polarization

5. A diffraction grating with a spacing of 15,000 lines/in. has a slit separation of
   (a) 6.67×10^{-6} in.   (b) 5.9×10^{-3} cm
   (c) $3.81 \ \mu m$ (d) 1.69×10^{-4} cm

6. In Young's experiment the slit separation is 0.02 nm, and the screen is 1 m away. If the slit is illuminated with light of wavelength 500 nm, the second bright fringe will be displaced from the central fringe by approximately
   (a) 3 cm   (b) 4 cm   (c) 5 cm   (d) 6 cm

7. A diffraction grating having 7000 lines/cm is illuminated by light of wavelength 589 nm. The angular separation of the second-order bright fringe is approximately
   (a) 51.2°   (b) 55.5°   (c) 61.5°   (d) 65°

8. A parallel beam of light illuminates a diffraction grating with 15,000 lines/in. The first-order image is located 16 cm from the central image of a screen 50 cm from the grating. The wavelength of the light is approximately
   (a) 515 nm   (b) 571 nm   (c) 541 nm   (d) 592 nm

9. A 30-in.-diameter optical telescope examines a large skylab orbiting 150 mi above the earth. The minimum separation of two points that can be resolved by the telescope, receiving light of average wavelength 500 nm, is approximately
(a) 0.56 ft   (b) 0.634 ft   (c) 0.75 ft   (d) 2.67 ft

10. In the previous example, the angular resolution is
(a) 8×10^{-7} rad   (b) 7.2×10^{-7} rad
(c) 8.1×10^{-6} rad   (d) 7.5×10^{-6} rad

COMPLETION QUESTIONS

1. The ability of waves to bend around obstacles in their path is called _____.

2. The minimum separation of two objects which can just be distinguished as separate images by a telescope is a measure of its _____.

3. A polarizer and an analyzer can be used to demonstrate that light waves are _____ waves.

4. The second bright line on either side of the central maximum for a diffraction grating is referred to as the _____ _____ fringe.

5. When two or more waves exist simultaneously in the same medium, the resultant _____ at any point is the sum of the _____ of the composite waves at that point.

6. The above represents a statement of the _____ principle.

7. The dark lines in Young's experiment are the result of _____ interference.

8. The resolving power of an instrument for use with light of constant wavelength is determined by the _____ of the objective lens.

9. An optical device which produces a spectrum as a result of interference of light passing through thousands of parallel slits is called a _____.

10. Two images are at the limit of resolution when the _____ _____ of one pattern coincides with the _____ fringe of the other pattern.

ANSWERS TO TRUE-FALSE, MULTIPLE CHOICE, AND COMPLETION QUESTIONS

1.	True	1.	c	1.	diffraction
2.	True	2.	a	2.	resolving power
3.	False	3.	b	3.	transverse
4.	True	4.	d	4.	second-order
5.	False	5.	d	5.	amplitude, amplitudes
6.	True	6.	c	6.	superposition
7.	False	7.	b	7.	destructive
8.	True	8.	a	8.	diameter
9.	True	9.	b	9.	diffraction grating
10.	True	10.	a	10.	central maximum, first dark

CHAPTER 30. ELECTRIC FORCE

CONTENTS

OBJECTIVES

You should be able to:

1. Demonstrate the existence of two kinds of charge and verify and explain the *first law of electrostatics* using a rubber rod, a glass rod, a piece of cat fur, a silk cloth, and a pith-ball electroscope.

2. Demonstrate the meaning of *positive* and *negative* charges as they apply to the transfer of electrons given a rubber rod, a piece of cat fur, and two suspended pith balls.

3. Define a *conductor* and an *insulator*, giving two examples of each.

4. Accomplish the following with a gold-leaf electroscope and other materials normally available in an electrostatics laboratory:
    (a) charge the electroscope negatively or positively by contact
    (b) charge the electroscope negatively or positively by induction
    (c) use the electroscope to determine the nature of an unknown charge

5. Explain with diagrams the initial attraction of uncharged material to a charged rod.

6. State Coulomb's law in your own words and write an equation representing the law.

7. Apply Coulomb's law to the solution of problems involving electro-static forces.

DEFINITIONS

Electrostatics - The science which treats electric charges at rest.

Charging - A process which transfers electrons in such a way that an excess or deficiency of electrons on a body results.

Negative charge - Electrification resulting from an excess of electrons.

Positive charge - Electrification which results from a deficiency of electrons.

Induced charge - Electrification resulting from a redistribution of charge due to the presence of a nearby charged object.

Conductor - A material through which charge can easily be transferred.

Electroscope - A laboratory device used to detect the presence of charge.

Insulator - A material which offers resistance to the flow of charge.

Coulomb's law - The force of attraction or repulsion between two point charges is directly proportional to the product of the two charges and inversely proportional to the square of the distance between them.

Coulomb - A unit of charge equivalent to 6.25×10^{18} electrons. It is the charge transferred through any cross section of a conductor in one second by a constant current of one ampere.

PHYSICAL CONCEPTS

1. An object which has an excess of electrons is said to be *negatively* charged, and an object which has a deficiency of electrons is said to be *positively* charged.

2. The first law of electrostatics states that *like charges repel each other and unlike charges attract each other*.

3. Coulomb's law states that *the force of attraction or repulsion between two point charges is directly proportional to the product of the two charges and inversely proportional to the separation of the two charges* (see Fig. 30-1).

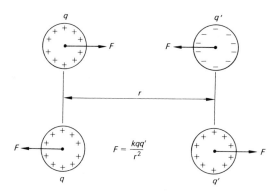

Fig. 30-1.

$$F = \frac{kqq'}{r^2} \qquad k = 9 \times 10^9 \text{ N·m}^2/\text{C}^2 \qquad \text{Coulomb's law}$$

The force F is in newtons (N) when the separation r is in meters (m) and the charge q is measured in coulombs (C).

4. When solving the problems in this chapter, it is important to use the *sign* of the charges to *determine* the direction of forces and Coulomb's law to determine their *magnitudes*. The resultant force on a particular charge is then found by the methods of vector mechanics.

TRUE-FALSE QUESTIONS

T   F   1. Rubbing a glass rod with a silk cloth leaves a negative charge on the cloth.

T   F   2. If two objects placed closely together repel each other electrically, we can be sure that they are *both* charged.

T   F   3. Bringing a negatively charged rod closer and closer to a positively charged electroscope causes the leaf to converge.

T   F   4. The process of charging an object by induction leaves a charge on that object which is opposite to that of the charging device.

T   F   5. Because of its large size, the coulomb is not a very practical unit for static electricity.

T   F   6. According to Coulomb's law, the electric force will be doubled if the separation of two equal charges is cut in half.

T   F   7. If two nearby objects experience a mutual force of electric attraction, they must *both* be electrically charged.

T   F   8. When two or more charges are in the vicinity of another charge, the latter charge experiences an electric force equal to the algebraic sum of the forces due to each charge.

T   F   9. The plus and minus signs used to identify charge have significance primarily for determining direction when applied to Coulomb's law.

T   F   10. One coulomb is that quantity of charge which when placed one meter away from an equal charge of the same sign will experience a repulsive force of one newton.

MULTIPLE-CHOICE QUESTIONS

1. A negatively charged body
   (a) has a deficiency of electrons
   (b) has an excess of electrons
   (c) is produced on glass by rubbing with silk
   (d) repels a positively charged body

2. Which of the following represents the largest measure of charge?
   (a) 1 μC (b) 1 nC
   (c) 10^{12} electrons   (d) 10^{-7} C

3. Charging a single body by induction always leaves a residual
   charge which is
   (a) greater than that of the charging object
   (b) of the same sign as that of the charging body
   (c) opposite in sign to that of the charging object
   (d) an excess of electrons

4. Decreasing the separation of two identical positive charges by
   one-half will cause the force of repulsion to change by a factor
   of
   (a) 4   (b) 2   (c) ½   (d) ¼

5. When two suspended objects are seen to attract each other
   electrically,
   (a) they are both charged   (b) one must be charged
   (c) either (a) or (b) is true   (d) neither (a) nor (b) is true

6. Two balls each having a charge of +12 μC are 8 cm apart. The
   electric force is approximately
   (a) 0.02 N   (b) 40 N   (c) 202 N   (d) 404 N

7. If a repulsive force of 2.0 N is observed between two identical
   9-μC charges, their separation must be approximately
   (a) 6 cm   (b) 3.6 cm   (c) 60 cm   (d) 36 cm

8. Three charges of +4, +8, and -2 nC are at the corners of an
   equilateral triangle 6 cm on a side. The magnitude of the force
   on the 8-nC charge is approximately
   (a) 6.93×10^{-5} N   (b) 3.47×10^{-5} N
   (c) 6×10^{-5} N   (d) 2.7×10^{-5} N

9. A charge of 6 μC is 10 cm to the right of a -4-μC charge. The
   resultant force on a 2-nC charge placed 4 cm to the right of the
   6-μC charge is
   (a) 4.75×10^{-2} N   (b) 8.75×10^{-2} N
   (c) 6.75×10^{-2} N   (d) 2×10^{-2} N

10. As a positively charged rod is brought closer and closer to a
    positively charged electroscope, the gold leaf
    (a) diverges   (b) converges
    (c) is neutralized   (d) is unaffected

COMPLETION QUESTIONS

1. An object which has an excess of electrons is _____
   charged and will repel a _____ charged body.

2. A _____ is a material through which charge may
   be easily transferred; whereas, an _____ resists
   the flow of charge.

3. A charge of 1 μC is equivalent to a charge of _____ C.

4. The first law of electrostatics states that like charges
   _____ and unlike charges _____.

5. Rubbing a wool cloth against a rubber rod transfers _____
   from the _____ to the _____.

6. The process of charging without the necessity of direct contact
   with a charged body is called _____.

7. According to _____ law, the electric force is
   inversely proportional to the square of the _____
   between two charges.

8. A charge of one coulomb is equivalent to that charge represented
   by _____ electrons.

9. The smallest unit of charge is the _____, which has a
   charge of _____ C.

10. The _____ is a laboratory device used to detect
    the presence of charge.

ANSWERS TO TRUE-FALSE, MULTIPLE CHOICE, AND COMPLETION QUESTIONS

1. True	1. b	1. negatively, negatively
2. True	2. a	2. conductor, insulator
3. True	3. c	3. 10^{-6}
4. True	4. a	4. repel, attract
5. True	5. c	5. electrons, cloth, rod
6. False	6. c	6. induction
7. False	7. c	7. Coulomb's, distance
8. False	8. a	8. 6.25×10^{18}
9. True	9. b	9. electron, 1.6×10^{-19}
10. False	10. a	10. electroscope

CHAPTER 31. ELECTRIC FIELD

CONTENTS

OBJECTIVES

You should be able to:

1. Define the *electric field* and state how the concept of a field is useful in describing electrical phenomena.

2. Produce an electric field, given a source of charge, an insulated metal sphere, and a suspended pith ball, and discuss the magnitude and direction of the field at specific points, demonstrating your knowledge by probing the field with a charged pith ball.

3. State two ways in which the electric field is similar to a gravitational field and two ways in which it differs.

4. Calculate the magnitude and direction of the force which would act on a known charge placed at a point where the electric field intensity is known.

5. Write an expression for the electric field intensity at a point a distance r from a charge Q and apply this equation in the solution of electrostatic problems.

6. Describe a procedure for calculating the resultant field intensity at a point in the vicinity of several known charges.

7. Explain and illustrate graphically the concept of electric field lines as a means of mapping the electric field intensity and state two rules which must be followed in the construction of electric field lines.

8. State *Gauss' law* in your own words, write an equation representing Gauss' law in mathematical symbols, and apply this law to the solution of problems.

9. State in 50 words or less the practical significance of Gauss' law in its application to real problems.

10. Describe or demonstrate in the laboratory Faraday's ice-pail experiment.

DEFINITIONS

Electric field - A region of space in which an electric charge will
    experience an electric force.

Electric field intensity - At a given point in space, the electric
    field intensity is the force per unit positive charge placed
    at that point.

Electric field lines - Imaginary lines describing the electric field
    in a region of space. They are drawn so that their direction
    at any point is the same as the direction of the field at that
    point.

Permittivity - A property of the medium surrounding a charge which
    is a measure of its ability to support an electric field.

Gauss' law - The net number of electric field lines crossing any
    closed surface in an outward direction is numerically equal to
    the net total charge within that surface.

Gaussian surface - An imaginary surface of simple geometric form,
    which is used in the application of Gauss' law.

PHYSICAL CONCEPTS

1. An electric field is said to exist in a region of space in which
    an electric charge will experience an electric force. The
    magnitude of the electric field intensity E is given by the force
    F per unit of charge q (see Fig. 31-1).

$$E = \frac{F}{q} \qquad E = \frac{kQ}{r^2} \qquad k = 9 \times 10^9 \text{ N·m}^2/\text{C}^2 \qquad \text{metric unit:} \quad \text{N/C}$$

    In this equation, r is the distance from the charge Q to the
    point in question.

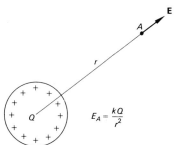

Fig. 31-1. Calculating the electric field intensity at a
            distance r from the center of a single charge Q.

2. The direction of the electric field intensity at a given point in space is the same as the direction in which a positive charge would move if it were placed at that point. The electric field intensity is a property of the *space* surrounding a charge or group of charges. It is not necessary for a charge to be placed at a point in order for a field to exist at that point.

3. The resultant field intensity at a point in the vicinity of a number of charges is the *vector sum* of the contributions from each charge.

$$E = E_1 + E_2 + E_3 + \cdots \qquad E = \Sigma \frac{kQ}{r^2} \qquad \text{vector sum}$$

It must be emphasized that this is a vector sum and not an algebraic sum. Once the magnitude and direction of each vector is determined, the resultant can be found from vector mechanics.

4. The permittivity of free space ε_0 is a fundamental constant defined as

$$\varepsilon_0 = \frac{1}{4\pi k} = 8.85 \times 10^{-12} \ C^2/N \cdot m^2 \qquad \text{permittivity}$$

5. Gauss' law states that the net number of electric field lines crossing any closed surface in an outward direction is numerically equal to the net total charge within that surface.

$$N = \Sigma \varepsilon_0 E_n A = \Sigma q \qquad \text{Gauss' law}$$

6. In applications of Gauss' law the concept of charge density σ as the charge q per unit area A of surface is often utilized:

$$\sigma = \frac{q}{A} \qquad q = \sigma A \qquad \text{charge density}$$

TRUE-FALSE QUESTIONS

T F 1. It is necessary that a charge be placed at a point in order to have an electric field at that point.

T F 2. Electric field lines never intersect.

T F 3. Gauss' law represents a statement of equality, but it will not withstand unit analysis.

T F 4. The direction of the electric field at a given point A in the vicinity of a positive charge depends on the sign of a charge placed at point A.

T F 5. The field in the vicinity of a number of charges is equal to the algebraic sum of the fields due to the individual charges.

T F 6. The spacing of electric field lines is such that they are close together when the field is strong and far apart when the field is weak.

T F 7. Gauss' law demonstrates that all of the charge lies on the surface of a conductor.

T F 8. Because of the way in which an electric field is defined, the direction of the electric field and the force on a test charge will always be the same.

T F 9. The electric field intensity at the midpoint of a line joining identical charges will always be zero.

T F 10. At a point twice as far away from a certain charge, the field intensity will be reduced by one-fourth.

MULTIPLE-CHOICE QUESTIONS

1. The electric field intensity is zero
   (a) midway between two equal charges of like sign
   (b) midway between two charges of unlike sign
   (c) at any point equal distances from two identical charges
   (d) between two equal but oppositely charged plates

2. The direction of the electric field intensity is
   (a) away from all negative charges
   (b) toward all negative charges
   (c) the same as the direction of an electric force
   (d) dependent on the nature of a charge placed at the point in question

3. The magnitude of the electric field does *not* depend on
   (a) the distance from charged objects
   (b) the sign of the charges causing the field
   (c) the magnitude of the charges causing the field
   (d) the force a unit positive charge will experience

4. The spacing of electric field lines between two identical point charges of opposite sign
   (a) is not dependent on the magnitude of the charges
   (b) is an indication of the field direction
   (c) is an indication of the field strength
   (d) is large when the charges are very large

5. According to Gauss' law, the number of electric field lines crossing any closed surface is
   (a) numerically equal to the enclosed charge
   (b) equal to the enclosed positive charge
   (c) equal to the electric field inside the surface
   (d) equal to the charge density on the surface

6. The permittivity of a medium
   (a) is a measure of its density
   (b) is equal to unity for air or a vacuum
   (c) is dependent on charge density of the medium
   (d) determines the magnitude of an electric field that can be established by the medium

7. The electric field intensity at a distance of 4 m from a 6-μC charge is
   (a) 1.69×10^3 N/C   (b) 3.38×10^3 N/C
   (c) 1.35×10^4 N/C   (d) 2×10^4 N/C

8. The electric field intensity between two oppositely charged plates is 4×10^5 N/C in a downward direction. The force on a -2-nC charge passing between the plates is
   (a) 2×10^4 N upward   (b) 2×10^4 N downward
   (c) 8×10^{-4} N upward   (d) 8×10^{-4} N downward

9. Two point charges of -4 and -6 μC are 10 cm apart in air. The magnitude of the electric field midway between the two charges is approximately
   (a) 7.2×10^6 N/C   (b) 3.6×10^7 N/C
   (c) 1.8×10^6 N/C   (d) 3.6×10^5 N/C

10. An 8-μC charge is 12 cm to the right of a -5-μC charge. The magnitude of the electric field at a point 9 cm above the 8-μC charge is approximately
    (a) 3.72 μN/C   (b) 5 μN/C   (c) 6.4 μN/C   (d) 7.43 μN/C

COMPLETION QUESTIONS

1. An electric field is said to exist in a region of space in which an _____ will experience an _____
   _____.

2. The direction of the _____
   at a point in space is the same as the direction in which a
   _____ would move if it were placed at
   that point.

3. The electric field intensity near a known charge is directly proportional to the _____ and
   inversely proportional to the _____
   _____.

168

4. When more than one charge contributes to a field, the resultant field at a point is the _____ of the fields due to each charge.

5. The spacing of electric field lines must be such that they are _____ where the field is weak and _____ _____ where the field is strong.

6. _____ are imaginary lines drawn so that their direction at any point is the same as the direction of the _____ at that point.

7. The direction of an electric field is _____ a positive charge and _____ a negative charge.

8. The total number of lines passing normally through a surface is numerically equal to the _____ contained within the surface. This is known as _____.

9. It can be shown from _____ that all charge resides on the _____ of a conductor.

10. The units of the proportionality constant k used in calculating the electric field intensity are _____.

ANSWERS TO TRUE-FALSE, MULTIPLE CHOICE, AND COMPLETION QUESTIONS

1. False	1. a	1. electric charge, electric force
2. True	2. b	
3. True	3. b	2. electric field intensity, positive charge
4. False	4. c	
5. False	5. a	3. magnitude of the charge, square of the distance from the charge
6. True	6. d	
7. True	7. b	
8. False	8. c	4. vector sum
9. True	9. a	5. far apart, close together
10. True	10. d	6. electric field lines, electric field
		7. away from, toward
		8. charge, Gauss' law
		9. Gauss' law, surface
		10. $N \cdot m^2/C^2$

CHAPTER 32. ELECTRIC POTENTIAL

CONTENTS

OBJECTIVES

You should be able to:

1. Distinguish between *positive work* and *negative work* and give a gravitational and electrical example of each.

2. Distinguish between *positive* and *negative potential energy*, giving gravitational and electrical examples.

3. Distinguish by definition and example between *potential energy*, *potential*, and *potential difference*.

4. Compute the potential energy of a known charge at a given distance from another known charge and state whether the potential energy is negative or positive.

5. Calculate the potential at any point due to a charge of known magnitude.

6. Compute the potential energy of a charge or the potential at a point in the neighborhood of a number of isolated charges.

7. Use your knowledge of potential difference to calculate the work required to move a known charge from any point A to another point B in an electric field created by one or more isolated point charges and state whether such work is done *by* the electric field or *on* the electric field.

8. Calculate the force which would be exerted on a given charge placed between two oppositely charged plates of known separation and potential difference.

9. Describe and illustrate Millikan's oil-drop experiment, stating its significance in the history of physics.

10. Define the *electronvolt* and be able to express energy in terms of this unit.

DEFINITIONS

Electric work - The scalar product of an electric force acting on a charge and the distance through which the charge is moved.

Electric potential energy - The negative of the work done by electric forces in moving a charge $+q$ from infinity to a given point. Conversely, it is equal to the work done by electric forces in removing the charge from the given point to infinity.

Electric potential - The potential energy per unit charge. It is the work per unit charge done by the electric field when a charge is removed to infinity from the point in question.

Volt - A unit of potential which represents work per unit charge equivalent to one joule per coulomb.

Potential difference - The work per unit positive charge done by electric forces in moving a test charge from the point of higher potential to the point of lower potential. It is sometimes referred to as voltage.

Potential gradient - The electric field expressed as a change in potential with distance. It is expressed in *volts per meter.* which is equivalent to newtons per coulomb.

Equipotential lines - Imaginary lines in an electrified space which connect points of equal potential. They are everywhere perpendicular to electric field lines.

Electronvolt - A unit of energy equivalent to the energy acquired by an electron which is accelerated through a potential difference of one volt.

PHYSICAL CONCEPTS

1. When a charge q is moved against a constant electric force for a distance d, the potential energy of the system is

$$\text{P.E.} = qEd$$

    where E is the constant electric field intensity. If the charge is released, it will acquire a kinetic energy

$$\text{K.E.} = \tfrac{1}{2}mv^2 = qEd$$

    as it returns for the same distance.

2. Due to the existence of positive and negative charges and the opposite effects produced by the same field, we must remember that:

    The potential energy increases as a positive charge is moved against the electric field, and the potential energy decreases as a negative charge is moved against the same field.

3. In general, the potential energy due to a charge q placed at a distance r from another charge Q is equal to the work done against electric forces in moving the charge $+q$ from infinity.

$$P.E. = \frac{kOq'}{r}$$ electric potential energy

Note that the distance r is not squared, as it was for the electric field intensity.

4. The electric *potential* V at a point a distance r from a charge Q is equal to the work per unit charge done against electric forces in bringing a positive charge $+q$ from infinity.

$$V = \frac{kQ}{r}$$ electric potential

The unit of electric potential is the joule per coulomb (J/C), which is renamed the volt (V).

$$1 \text{ V} = \frac{1 \text{ J}}{1 \text{ C}}$$

5. The potential at a point in the vicinity of a number of charges is equal to the algebraic sum of the potentials due to each charge:

$$V = \Sigma \frac{kQ}{r} = \frac{kQ_1}{r_1} + \frac{kQ_2}{r_2} + \frac{kQ_3}{r_3} + \cdots$$ algebraic sum

6. The potential difference between two points A and B is the difference in the potentials at those points.

$$V_{AB} = V_A - V_B$$ potential difference

The work done by an electric field in moving a charge q from point A to point B can be found from

$$\text{Work}_{AB} = q(V_A - V_B)$$ work and potential difference

7. The potential difference between two oppositely charged plates is equal to the product of the field intensity and the plate separation.

$$V = Ed \qquad E = \frac{V}{d}$$

The *potential gradient* is the electric field intensity expressed in volts per meter (V/m).

TRUE-FALSE QUESTIONS

T F 1. When the electric field does negative work in moving a charge from infinity to point B, the potential energy of the charge at B will also be negative.

T F 2. The electric potential energy is positive in the vicinity of a positive charge and negative in the vicinity of a negative charge.

T F 3. Electric potential at a point is a property of the space whereas electric potential energy cannot exist unless a charge is placed at that point.

T F 4. Whenever a negative charge is moved from a point of high potential to a point of low potential, its potential energy is increased.

T F 5. The electric potential in the vicinity of a number of charges is equal to the algebraic sum of the potentials due to each charge.

T F 6. A negative potential means that the electric field will hold on to positive charge, and work must be done by an external agent to remove it.

T F 7. If the potential is zero at a point, the electric field must also be zero at that point.

T F 8. The electric field between two oppositely charged plates is equal to the product of the voltage and the plate separation.

T F 9. The electronvolt is a unit of potential difference.

T F 10. The surface of any conductor is an equipotential surface.

MULTIPLE-CHOICE QUESTIONS

1. When a negative charge is moved from a point of low potential to a point of high potential,
   (a) its potential energy increases
   (b) its potential energy decreases
   (c) no work is done by the field
   (d) positive work is done by the field

2. The potential energy at a given point is independent of
   (a) the work required to bring a charge to that point
   (b) the electric field
   (c) the path taken to reach that point
   (d) the magnitude of a charge at that point

3. In the vicinity of a negative charge,
   (a) the potential is always negative
   (b) the potential energy is always negative
   (c) the potential energy is always positive
   (d) the potential is always positive

4. Which of the following represents a unit of energy?
   (a) V   (b) N/C   (c) J/C   (d) eV

5. The Millikan oil-drop experiment was used primarily to determine
   (a) the mass of an electron
   (b) the charge of an electron
   (c) the ratio of charge to mass for an electron
   (d) the density of oil

6. The electric potential is zero
   (a) inside a conductor
   (b) midway between any two charges of opposite sign
   (c) midway between two equal charges of same sign
   (d) at any point equal distances from equal charges of opposite
       sign

7. A 3-nC charge is located 2 m away from another charge of 40 μC.
   The potential energy of the smaller charge is
   (a) 1.8×10^{-4} J   (b) 2.7×10^{-4} J
   (c) 5.4×10^{-4} J   (d) 6.9×10^{-4} J

8. A charge of +4 μC is 10 cm to the right of a -12-μC charge. The
   electric potential at a point midway between the two charges is
   approximately
   (a) 1.44 μV   (b) -1.44 μV   (c) 72 μV   (d) -2.16 μV

9. Points A and B are located 6 and 10 cm away from a -24-μC charge.
   The potential difference $V_A - V_B$ between A and B is approximately
   (a) -1.44 μV   (b) 1.44 μV   (c) -5.04 μV   (d) 5.04 μV

10. A 16-μC charge is located 8 cm to the right of a -8-μC charge.
    How much work will be done by the electric field in moving a
    2-nC charge from a point midway between the two charges to a
    point 4 cm to the left of the -8-μC charge?
    (a) 2.4 mJ   (b) 4.8 mJ   (c) -2.4 mJ   (d) -4.8 mJ

COMPLETION QUESTIONS

1. The _____ at a point is equal to the negative
   of the work per unit charge done by electric forces in bringing
   a positive charge from infinity.

2. The potential in the vicinity of a positive charge is _____, and the potential in the vicinity of a negative charge is

   _____.

3. The potential in the vicinity of a number of charges is equal to the _____ of the potentials due to each charge.

4. A potential of 1 V means that a charge of _____ will have a potential energy of _____ when placed at that point.

5. The potential difference between two oppositely charged plates is equal to the product of the _____ and the _____.

6. The _____ is a unit of energy equivalent to the energy acquired by an electron which is accelerated through a potential difference of one volt.

7. The work done by an electric field in moving a charge from a point of potential V_A to a point of potential V_B is equal to the product of _____ and _____.

8. The volt per meter is a unit of _____ _____ and is equivalent to the unit _____.

9. A _____ potential energy means that work must be done _____ the electric field in removing a charge from the field.

10. Whenever a positive charge is moved against the electric field, its potential energy _____; whenever a negative charge moves against an electric field, its potential energy

    _____.

ANSWERS TO TRUE-FALSE, MULTIPLE CHOICE, AND COMPLETION QUESTIONS

1.	False	1.	b	1.	potential
2.	False	2.	c	2.	positive, negative
3.	True	3.	a	3.	algebraic sum
4.	True	4.	d	4.	1 C, 1 J
5.	True	5.	b	5.	field intensity, plate
6.	True	6.	d		separation
7.	False	7.	c	6.	electronvolt
8.	False	8.	b	7.	q, $V_A - V_B$
9.	False	9.	a		
10.	True	10.	b	8.	electric field intensity, newtons per coulomb
				9.	negative, against; or positive, by
				10.	increases, decreases

175

CHAPTER 33. CAPACITANCE

CONTENTS

OBJECTIVES

You should be able to:

1. Define the *dielectric strength* of a material and describe the part it plays in limiting the charge which can be placed on a conductor.

2. State the effects of the size and shape of a conductor on its ability to store charge.

3. Demonstrate your understanding of *capacitance*.

4. State and apply a relationship between *capacitance, applied voltage,* and *total charge.*

5. Compute the capacitance of a parallel-plate capacitor when the area of the plates and their separation in a medium of known dielectric constant are given.

6. State three advantages realized by insertion of a dielectric between the plates of a capacitor.

7. Write expressions for calculating the dielectric constant as a function of the voltage, the electric field, or the capacitance before and after insertion of a dielectric.

8. Define *permittivity* and give an example illustrating its effect on capacitance.

9. Calculate the equivalent capacitance of a number of capacitors connected in series or in parallel.

10. Solve for the charge and voltage across capacitors connected in series and in parallel.

11. Determine the energy of a charged capacitor, given the appropriate parameters.

DEFINITIONS

Dielectric - An insulator, or a material containing very few charges free to move.

Dielectric strength - For a given material, the electric field intensity for which that material ceases to be an insulator and becomes a conductor.

Capacitor - Two closely spaced conductors carrying equal and opposite charges.

Capacitance - For a single conductor, the ratio of the charge on the conductor to the potential produced; for a capacitor, the ratio of the charge on either plate to the resulting potential difference between the plates.

Farad - A capacitor has a capacitance of one farad if an increase in charge of one coulomb results in an increase in potential difference of one volt.

Dielectric constant - A property of a dielectric equal to the ratio of the capacitance of a capacitor with the dielectric to its capacitance for a vacuum.

Permittivity - A property of a material which is a measure of its ability to establish an electric field.

Relative permittivity - The ratio of the permittivity of a material to the permittivity of a vacuum. It is equal to the dielectric constant of that material.

Series connection - A group of capacitors connected along a single path.

Parallel connection - A group of capacitors connected directly to the same source of potential difference so that the same voltage is applied to each capacitor.

PHYSICAL CONCEPTS

1. Capacitance is the ratio of charge Q to the potential V for a given conductor. For two oppositely charged plates, the Q refers to the charge on either plate and the V refers to the potential difference between the plates.

$$C = \frac{Q}{V} \qquad 1 \text{ farad (F)} = \frac{1 \text{ coulomb (C)}}{1 \text{ volt (V)}} \qquad \text{capacitance}$$

177

2. The dielectric strength is that value for E for which a given material ceases to be an insulator and becomes a conductor. For air this value is

$$E = \frac{kQ}{r^2} = 3 \times 10^6 \text{ N/C} \qquad \text{dielectric strength, air}$$

3. For a parallel-plate capacitor, the material between the plates is called the dielectric. The insertion of such a material has an effect on the electric field and the potential between the plates. Consequently, it changes the capacitance. The dielectric constant K for a particular material is the ratio of the capacitance with the dielectric C to the capacitance for a vacuum C_0.

$$K = \frac{C}{C_0} \qquad K = \frac{V_0}{V} \qquad K = \frac{E}{E_0} \qquad \text{dielectric constant}$$

4. The permittivity of a dielectric is greater than the permittivity of a vacuum by a factor equal to the dielectric constant. For this reason, K is sometimes referred to as the *relative permittivity*.

$$K = \frac{\varepsilon}{\varepsilon_0} \qquad \varepsilon = K\varepsilon_0 \qquad \varepsilon_0 = 8.85 \times 10^{-12} \text{ C}^2/\text{N}\cdot\text{m}^2$$

5. The capacitance for a parallel-plate capacitor depends on the surface area A of each plate, the plate separation d, and the permittivity or dielectric constant. The general equation is

$$C = \varepsilon \frac{A}{d} \qquad C = K\varepsilon_0 \frac{A}{d} \qquad \text{capacitance}$$

For a vacuum, $K = 1$, in the above relationship.

6. Capacitors may be connected in series as shown in Fig. 33-1a or in parallel as shown in Fig. 33-1b.

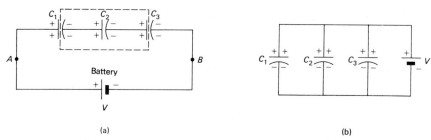

(a)   (b)

Fig. 33-1. (a) Series connection of capacitors; (b) parallel connection of capacitors.

178

(a) For *series connections*, the charge on each capacitor is the same as the total charge, the potential difference across the battery is equal to the sum of the drops across each capacitor, and the net capacitance is found from

$$Q_T = Q_1 = Q_2 = Q_3 \qquad V_T = V_1 + V_2 + V_3$$

$$\frac{1}{C_e} = \frac{1}{C_1} + \frac{1}{C_2} + \frac{1}{C_3} \qquad \text{series connections}$$

(b) For *parallel connections*, the total charge is equal to the sum of the charges across each capacitor, the voltage drop across each capacitor is the same as the drop across the battery, and the effective capacitance is equal to the sum of the individual capacitances.

$$Q_T = Q_1 + Q_2 + Q_3 \qquad V_B = V_1 = V_2 = V_3$$

$$C_e = C_1 + C_2 + C_3 \qquad \text{parallel connections}$$

7. The potential energy stored in a charged capacitor can be found from any of the following relationships:

$$\text{P.E.} = \tfrac{1}{2}QV \qquad \text{P.E.} = \tfrac{1}{2}CV^2 \qquad \text{P.E.} = \frac{Q^2}{2C}$$

When C is in *farads*, V is in *volts*, and Q is in *coulombs*, the potential energy will be in *joules*.

TRUE-FALSE QUESTIONS

T F 1. The total capacitance of two capacitors connected in series is less than that of either capacitor alone.

T F 2. The capacitance is dependent on the potential difference placed across its plates.

T F 3. If a conductor has a capacitance of one farad, a transfer of one coulomb of charge to the conductor will increase its potential by one volt.

T F 4. The amount of charge which can be placed on a spherical conductor is a function of its size and shape but not the surrounding medium.

T F 5. For capacitors connected in parallel, the charge on each capacitor will be equal.

T F 6. The capacitance of a given capacitor will be higher if the separation of the plates is reduced without changing the dielectric.

179

T F 7. Insertion of a dielectric between the plates of a capacitor decreases the voltage across it and hence reduces the capacitance.

T F 8. If the charge on a capacitor is doubled, the potential energy will be quadrupled.

T F 9. For capacitors connected in parallel, the voltage across each capacitor is the same as that across the source.

T F 10. The dielectric constant is also the relative permittivity.

MULTIPLE-CHOICE QUESTIONS

1. The amount of charge which can be placed on a conductor does not depend on
   (a) the dielectric strength of the surrounding medium
   (b) its capacitance
   (c) its potential
   (d) its size or shape

2. The capacitance of a capacitor increases with a decrease in
   (a) dielectric constant   (b) permittivity
   (c) plate area   (d) plate separation

3. Which of the following is not a representation of the potential energy of a conductor?
   (a) $\frac{1}{2}QV^2$ (b) $Q^2/2C$ (c) $\frac{1}{2}QV$ (d) $\frac{1}{2}CV^2$

4. Which of the following is true for capacitors in series?
   (a) The total capacitance is the sum of the individual capacitances.
   (b) The total charge is the sum of the charges on each capacitor.
   (c) The total voltage is the sum of the voltages across each capacitor.
   (d) The available charge is shared between two or more capacitors.

5. Which of the following is not equal to the dielectric constant?
   (a) V_0/V (b) C_0/C (c) E_0/E (d) $\varepsilon_0/\varepsilon$

6. The plates of a 2-pF capacitor have an area of 20 cm^2. If air is the dielectric, the plate separation must be approximately
   (a) 0.885 mm   (b) 8.85 mm   (c) 88.5 mm   (d) 885 mm

7. What potential difference is required to store 24 µC of charge on a 6-µF capacitor?
   (a) 4 V   (b) 0.25 V   (c) 40 V   (d) 144 V

8. The voltage across the 3-µF capacitor in Fig. 33-2 is
   (a) 4 V   (b) 6 V   (c) 8 V   (d) 12 V

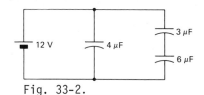

Fig. 33-2.

9. A certain capacitor has a capacitance of 12 μF when the dielectric is air. The capacitor is charged to 400 V and disconnected from the power source. If a dielectric (K = 4.0) is inserted, the new voltage will be
   (a) 100 V   (b) 400 V   (c) 800 V   (d) 1600 V

10. An 8-μF capacitor is connected to a potential difference of 12 V. The potential energy is
    (a) 4.8×10^{-4} J   (b) 5.76×10^{-4} J
    (c) 576 J   (d) 480 J

COMPLETION QUESTIONS

1. The capacitance of a given capacitor will be directly proportional to the _____ of the plates and inversely proportional to _____.

2. The _____ for a given material is that electric field intensity for which the material ceases to be an insulator and becomes a conductor.

3. Three advantages for the use of dielectrics with capacitors are _____, _____ _____, and _____.

4. Three different physical ratios which can be used to calculate the dielectric constant are _____, _____, and _____.

5. The dielectric constant may also be referred to as the relative _____ of a material.

6. The total capacitance of a number of capacitors connected in series is _____ (less than, greater than, or the same as) the capacitance of any capacitor taken individually.

7. After a capacitor is charged and removed from the source of emf, insertion of a dielectric will cause the potential across the plates to _____.

8. The _____ for a material is the ratio of the capacitance with that material between the plates to the capacitance for a vacuum between the plates.

9. For a given capacitor of known charge Q, voltage V, and capacitance C, list three expressions for calculating its potential energy: _____, _____, and _____.

10. A group of capacitors connected directly to the same source of potential difference so that the available charge is shared are said to be connected in _____.

ANSWERS TO TRUE-FALSE, MULTIPLE CHOICE AND COMPLETION QUESTIONS

1.	True	1.	c	1.	area, their separation
2.	False	2.	d	2.	dielectric strength
3.	True	3.	a	3.	small plate separation,
4.	False	4.	c		increased capacitance, higher
5.	False	5.	b		breakdown voltage
6.	True	6.	b	4.	C/C_0, V_0/V, E_0/E
7.	False	7.	a	5.	permittivity
8.	True	8.	c	6.	less than
9.	True	9.	a	7.	drop
10.	True	10.	b	8.	dielectric constant
				9.	$\frac{1}{2}QV$, $\frac{1}{2}CV^2$, $Q^2/2C$
				10.	parallel

CHAPTER 34.   CURRENT AND RESISTANCE

CONTENTS

OBJECTIVES

You should be able to:

1. Define the *ampere* as a unit of electric current and demonstrate your understanding by drawing an analogy to water flowing through a pipe.

2. Distinguish between *electron flow* and *conventional current,* illustrating your understanding with simple diagrams.

3. Define *electromotive force* and discuss the part it plays in dc electricity.

4. State *Ohm's law* both verbally and mathematically and apply this law to the solution of electrical problems involving resistance.

5. Demonstrate Ohm's law with a voltmeter, an ammeter, a rheostat, a source of emf, and appropriate lead wires and draw a schematic diagram of your setup, using appropriate symbols for electrical equipment.

6. Compute power losses in a given electric circuit when any two of the following quantities are known: (a) the voltage, (b) the current, and (c) the resistance.

7. State four factors which determine the resistance of a given wire.

8. Define *resistivity* and show by an equation how it can be used to calculate electrical resistance.

9. Calculate the length of wire required to produce a given resistance, given a supply of wire of known resistivity and cross-sectional area.

10. Define the *circular mil* (cmil) as a unit of cross-sectional area and use it in calculating electrical resistance.

11. Define *temperature coefficient of resistance* and write an equation for its computation.

12. Calculate the change in resistance which occurs as a result of a change in temperature of a wire.

183

DEFINITIONS

Electric current - The rate of flow of charge Q past a given point P on an electrical conductor. The units are the coulomb per second.

Ampere - A unit of electric current representing a flow of charge at the rate of one coulomb per second.

Source of electromotive force - A device which converts chemical, mechanical, or other forms of energy necessary to maintain a continuous flow of electric charge.

Electromotive force (emf) - The work per unit charge (J/C) required to maintain a continuous flow of charge.

Ohm's law - The current produced in a given conductor is directly proportional to the difference of potential between its end points.

Electrical resistance - The opposition a material offers to the flow of charge. A resistance of one ohm will support a current of one ampere for a difference of potential of one volt.

Electric power - The rate at which charge gains or loses energy.

Resistivity - The property of a material which determines its electrical resistance at a given temperature.

Temperature coefficient of resistance - The change in resistance per unit resistance per degree change in temperature.

Circular mil - The cross-sectional area of a wire which is 1 mil (0.001 in.) in diameter.

PHYSICAL CONCEPTS

1. Electric current I is the rate of flow of charge Q past a given point on a conductor:

$$I = \frac{Q}{t} \qquad 1 \text{ ampere (A)} = \frac{1 \text{ coulomb (C)}}{1 \text{ second (s)}}$$

2. By convention, the *direction* of electric current is the same as the direction in which *positive* charges would move, even if the actual current consists of a flow of negatively charged electrons.

3. Ohm's law states that *the current produced in a given conductor is directly proportional to the difference of potential between its endpoints:*

$$R = \frac{V}{I} \qquad V = IR \qquad \text{Ohm's law}$$

The symbol R represents the resistance in ohms (Ω) defined as

$$1 \text{ ohm } (\Omega) = \frac{1 \text{ ampere (A)}}{1 \text{ volt (V)}}$$

4. The electric power in watts is given by any of

$$P = VI \qquad P = I^2R \qquad P = \frac{V^2}{R} \qquad \text{power}$$

5. The resistance of a wire depends on four factors: (a) the kind of *material*, (b) the *length*, (c) the cross-sectional *area*, and the *temperature*. By introducing a property of the material called its *resistivity* ρ, we can write

$$R = \rho\frac{l}{A} \qquad \rho = \frac{RA}{l} \qquad \text{SI unit for } \rho: \quad \Omega\cdot m$$

6. The *temperature coefficient of resistance* α is the change in resistance per unit resistance per degree change in temperature.

$$\alpha = \frac{\Delta R}{R_0 \, \Delta t} \qquad \Delta R = \alpha R_0 \, \Delta t$$

TRUE-FALSE QUESTIONS

T F 1. The electromotive force is a force exerted on an electric charge to keep it moving.

T F 2. The direction of conventional current for a conductor is opposite to the direction of electron flow.

T F 3. Electric current is also a measure of the average speed with which electrons move in a conductor.

T F 4. According to Ohm's law, the electric current is inversely proportional to the applied voltage.

T F 5. Electrical resistance increases with an increase in the cross-sectional area of a conductor.

T F 6. The resistivity of a wire is independent of the length of the wire.

T F 7. A wire having a diameter of 0.002 in. has a cross-sectional area of 4 cmils.

T F 8. The temperature coefficient of resistance is equal to the change in resistance per degree change in temperature.

T F 9. The power loss in a wire is quadrupled if the current is doubled.

T F 10. A rheostat is a meter which indicates the electrical resistance in a circuit.

MULTIPLE-CHOICE QUESTIONS

1. A unit of electromotive force is the
   (a) joule   (b) newton   (c) volt   (d) watt

2. If one were to use a water analogy to study electric current, voltage would be most similar to
   (a) force   (b) pressure
   (c) rate of flow   (d) density

3. The resistance of a wire is not dependent on its
   (a) temperature   (b) length
   (c) area   (d) current

4. Which of the following is not a measure of electric power?
   (a) VR^2 (b) VI (c) I^2R (d) V^2/R

5. Which of the following is not a unit of resistivity?
   (a) $\Omega \cdot cm$ (b) $\Omega \cdot cmil/ft$ (c) Ω/ft (d) $\Omega \cdot m$

6. The potential difference between the terminals of a small heater is 60 V. If the resistance of the heater is 30 Ω, the current is
   (a) 0.5 A   (b) 2 A   (c) 1800 A   (d) 3 A

7. An emf of 12 V will move 6.25 x 10^{18} electrons past a given point in 2 s. The resistance is
   (a) 24 Ω (b) 121 Ω (c) 6 Ω (d) 3.84 Ω

8. A 120-V heater has a resistance of 600 Ω. The heat energy generated in 1 min is
   (a) 24 J   (b) 120 J   (c) 1200 J   (d) 1440 J

9. An aluminum wire has a resistivity of 17 $\Omega \cdot cmils/ft$ and a cross-sectional diameter of 0.2 in. What length of this wire is needed to construct a 1700-Ω resistor?
   (a) 200 ft   (b) 144.5 ft   (c) 4 x 10^6 ft   (d) 2 x 10^4 ft

10. The temperature coefficient of resistance for copper is 0.004/C°. If the resistance of a copper wire is 12 Ω at 20°C, its resistance at 100°C will be
    (a) 3.8 Ω (b) 13 Ω (c) 15.84 Ω (d) 50.4 Ω

COMPLETION QUESTIONS

1. A source of emf of one _____ will perform one _____ of _____ on each coulomb of charge which passes through it.

2. The current in a resistor is directly proportional to the
_____ and inversely proportional to the _____.
This is a statement of _____.

3. Four factors which affect the resistance of a wire are
_____, _____, _____, and
_____.

4. The temperature coefficient of resistance is the change in
_____ per unit _____ per unit change in
_____.

5. The rate of heat loss in a wire can be found from the product
of the _____ and the square of the _____.

6. The direction of conventional current is always the same as the
direction in which _____ would move.

7. The area of a wire in _____ equals the
square of the _____ in mils.

8. The resistance of a conductor at a given temperature is directly
proportional to its _____, inversely proportional to its
_____, and dependent on a material constant called its
_____.

9. Three laboratory devices used to study resistance, current, and
voltage are _____, _____, and _____,
respectively.

10. A source of electromotive force can convert _____
_____ energy into _____ energy.

ANSWERS TO TRUE-FALSE, MULTIPLE CHOICE, AND COMPLETION QUESTIONS

1.	False	1.	c	1.	volt, joule, work
2.	True	2.	b	2.	voltage, resistance, Ohm's law
3.	False	3.	d	3.	length, area, temperature,
4.	False	4.	a		material
5.	False	5.	c	4.	resistance, resistance,
6.	True	6.	b		temperature
7.	True	7.	a	5.	resistance, current
8.	False	8.	d	6.	positive charges
9.	True	9.	c	7.	circular mils, diameter
10.	False	10.	c	8.	length, area, resistivity
				9.	rheostats, ammeters,
					voltmeters
				10.	mechanical or chemical,
					electrical

CHAPTER 35.   DIRECT-CURRENT CIRCUITS

CONTENTS

OBJECTIVES

You should be able to:

1. Connect resistors in series or in parallel and construct circuit diagrams for each connection.

2. Write statements describing voltage, current, and equivalent resistance for resistors connected in series and for resistors connected in parallel.

3. Calculate the effective resistance of a group of resistors connected in series or in parallel.

4. Determine the current and voltage for each resistor in a circuit containing known resistors connected in series and in parallel with a known source of emf.

5. Distinguish between *emf* and *terminal potential difference,* writing an equation which expresses their relationship as a function of internal resistance.

6. Predict the terminal voltage, given the emf of a battery, its internal resistance, and the load resistance.

7. Suggest an experiment which will measure the internal resistance of a battery.

8. Calculate for a circuit containing one or more sources of emf the net current delivered to the circuit and the terminal voltage for each source of emf.

9. State and apply Kirchhoff's laws for electrical networks in the determination of unknown currents.

10. Determine the magnitude of the unknown resistance when an unknown resistor and a Wheatstone bridge are given.

DEFINITIONS

Series connection - Two or more elements are said to be in series
    if they have only one point in common that is not connected to
    some third element. For resistors, a series connection provides
    only one path for current.

Parallel connection - A connection of resistors in which the current
    may be divided between two or more elements.

DC circuit - An electric circuit in which there is a continuous flow
    of charge in only one direction.

Terminal potential difference - The actual potential difference
    representing the external voltage drop across the terminals of a
    source of emf.

Internal resistance - The inherent resistance within every source
    of emf.

Kirchhoff's first law - The sum of the currents entering a junction
    is equal to the sum of the currents leaving that junction.

Kirchhoff's second law - The sum of the emfs around any closed
    current loop is equal to the sum of all the IR drops around
    that loop.

Wheatstone bridge - A laboratory apparatus which measures an unknown
    resistance by varying known resistances until the system is
    balanced.

PHYSICAL CONCEPTS

1. In dc circuits, resistors may be connected in series, as shown in
    Fig. 35-1a, or in parallel, as in Fig. 35-1b.

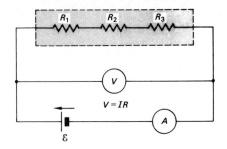

(a) Series connection

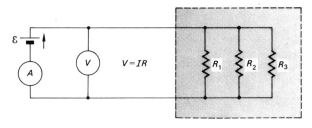

(b) Parallel connection

Fig. 35-1. Series and parallel connections of resistors.

(a) For *series connections*, the current in all parts of the circuit is the same, the total voltage drop is the sum of the individual drops across each resistor, and the effective resistance is equal to the sum of the individual resistances:

$$I_T = I_1 = I_2 = I_3 \qquad V_T = V_1 + V_2 + V_3$$

$$R_e = R_1 + R_2 + R_3 \qquad \text{series connections}$$

(b) For *parallel connections*, the total current is the sum of the individual currents, the voltage drops are all equal, and the effective resistance is given by

$$I_T = I_1 + I_2 + I_3 \qquad V_T = V_1 = V_2 = V_3$$

$$\frac{1}{R_e} = \frac{1}{R_1} + \frac{1}{R_2} + \frac{1}{R_3} \qquad \text{parallel connections}$$

For two resistors connected in parallel, a simpler form is

$$R_e = \frac{R_1 R_2}{R_1 + R_2} \qquad \text{two resistors in parallel}$$

190

2. The current supplied to an electric circuit is equal to the *net* emf divided by the total resistance of the circuit, including internal resistances.

$$I = \frac{\Sigma E}{\Sigma R} \qquad \text{for example, } I = \frac{E_1 - E_2}{r_1 + r_2 + R_L}$$

The example is for two opposing batteries of internal resistances r_1 and r_2 when the circuit load resistance is R_L.

3. According to Kirchhoff's laws, the current entering a junction must equal the current leaving the junction and the net emf around any loop must equal the sum of the *IR* drops. Symbolically,

$$\Sigma I_{entering} = \Sigma I_{leaving}$$
$$\Sigma E = \Sigma IR$$

Kirchhoff's laws

4. The following steps should be applied in solving circuits with Kirchhoff's laws (see Fig. 35-2):

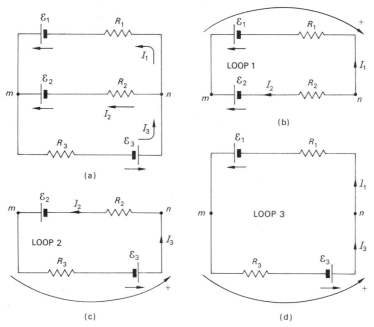

Fig. 35-2.

Step 1. *Assume a current direction for each loop in the network.*

Step 2. *Apply Kirchhoff's first law to write a current equation for all but one of the junction points* $\left(\Sigma I_{in} = \Sigma I_{out}\right)$.

Step 3. *Indicate by a small arrow the direction in which each emf acting alone would cause a + charge to move.*

191

Step 4. *Apply Kirchhoff's second law* ($\Sigma E = \Sigma IR$) *to write an equation for all possible current loops.* An arbitrary positive tracing direction is chosen. An emf is considered + if its output direction is the same as your tracing direction. An *IR* drop is considered + when the assumed current direction is the same as your tracing direction.

Step 5. *Solve the equations simultaneously to determine the unknown quantities.*

5. A Wheatstone bridge is a device which allows one to determine an unknown resistance R_x by balancing the voltage drops in the circuit. If R_3 is known and the ratio R_2/R_1 can be determined, we have

$$\overline{R_x = R_3 \frac{R_2}{R_1}}$$ the Wheatstone bridge

TRUE-FALSE QUESTIONS

T   F   1.   The rules for computing equivalent resistance are the same as those for computing equivalent capacitance.

T   F   2.   The current in all parts of a parallel circuit is the same.

T   F   3.   The equivalent resistance of two resistors in parallel is equal to their product divided by their sum.

T   F   4.   The emf is essentially equal to the open-circuit potential difference.

T   F   5.   The current supplied to an electric circuit is equal to the net emf divided by the total resistance of the circuit if we neglect internal resistance.

T   F   6.   Kirchhoff's second law applies for each current loop in a complex circuit and not just for the total circuit.

T   F   7.   In applying Kirchhoff's laws, the tracing direction must be the same as the current direction.

T   F   8.   When the Wheatstone bridge is balanced, the voltage between the galvanometer and either terminal of the source of emf will be the same.

T   F   9.   Kirchhoff's laws apply only for current loops which contain at least one source of emf.

T   F   10. When two identical resistors are connected in parallel, the voltage drop across each is one half of the terminal potential difference at the source of emf.

MULTIPLE-CHOICE QUESTIONS

1. The variance of terminal potential difference, as compared with
   emf, is due to
   (a) the circuit load   (b) the internal resistance
   (c) Kirchhoff's law   (d) current delivered

2. For a parallel circuit, which of the following is not true?
   (a) The current through each resistance is the same.
   (b) The voltage across each resistance is the same.
   (c) The total current is equal to the sum of the currents
       through each resistance.
   (d) The reciprocal of the equivalent resistance is equal to the
       sum of the reciprocals of the individual resistances.

3. Which of the following is not affected by internal resistance?
   (a) terminal potential difference
   (b) emf of the source
   (c) current delivered to external circuit
   (d) power output

4. If a circuit contains three loops, how many *independent* equations
   can be obtained with Kirchhoff's two laws?
   (a) three   (b) four   (c) five   (d) six

5. In using the Wheatstone bridge, the quantity that is balanced is
   (a) voltage   (b) resistance (c) current   (d) emf

6. For the circuit in Fig. 35-3, the equivalent external resistance
   is approximately
   (a) 1.8 Ω   (b) 4 Ω   (c) 6 Ω   (d) 20 Ω

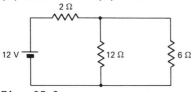

Fig. 35-3.

7. In Fig. 35-3, if we neglect internal resistance, the current
   through the 6-Ω resistance is
   (a) 1.0 A   (b) 1.33 A   (c) 1.67 A   (d) 2 A

8. The terminal voltage for the source of emf in Fig. 35-4 is
   (a) 24 V   (b) 22 V   (c) 21.8 V   (d) 20 V

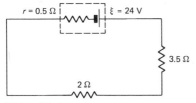

Fig. 35-4.

9. The current through the 4-Ω resistance in Fig. 35-5, as found from Kirchhoff's laws, is
(a) 1 A   (b) 1.5 A   (c) 2 A   (d) 2.5 A

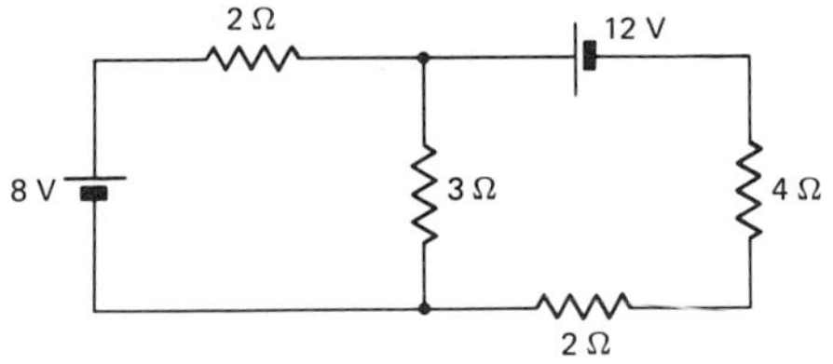

Fig. 35-5.

10. A Wheatstone bridge is used to measure the unknown resistance R_x of a coil of wire. The resistance box is adjusted for 8 Ω, and the galvanometer indicates zero current when the contact key is positioned at the 40-cm mark. The unknown resistance is
(a) 5.33 Ω
(b) 12 Ω
(c) neither (a) nor (b)
(d) either (a) or (b) depending on hookup

COMPLETION QUESTIONS

1. The type of connection appropriate for most household electrical devices would be a _____ connection.

2. For a series connection, the _____ is constant throughout the circuit, but the total _____ is the sum of the individual circuit values.

3. The _____ is equal to the emf of a battery less the voltage drop across the internal resistance.

4. As a battery ages, its terminal potential difference decreases because of _____.

5. State Kirchhoff's first law: _____
_____.
State Kirchhoff's second law: _____
_____.

6. When current is reversed through a source of emf against its normal output direction, the terminal potential difference is equal to _____, where E represents emf and r the internal resistance.

7. When summing the emfs around a loop for Kirchhoff's law, the value for emf is considered _____ if its normal output is against the tracing direction.

8. If a negative value is obtained for a current from Kirchhoff's method, it represents an error in _____ only.

9. The current supplied to an electric circuit is equal to the net _____ divided by the total _____ of the circuit, including _____ resistance.

10. The _____ is a laboratory device for measuring resistance.

ANSWERS TO TRUE-FALSE, MULTIPLE CHOICE, AND COMPLETION QUESTIONS

1.	False	1.	b	1.	parallel
2.	False	2.	a	2.	current, voltage
3.	True	3.	b	3.	terminal potential difference
4.	True	4.	b	4.	an increase in internal
5.	False	5.	a		resistance
6.	True	6.	c	5.	$\Sigma I_{entering} = \Sigma I_{leaving}$;
7.	False	7.	b		
8.	True	8.	b		$\Sigma E = \Sigma IR$
9.	False	9.	a	6.	$E + Ir$
10.	False	10.	d	7.	negative
				8.	direction
				9.	emf, resistance, internal
				10.	Wheatstone bridge

CHAPTER 36.   ELECTROCHEMISTRY; THERMOELECTRICITY

CONTENTS

OBJECTIVES

You should be able to:

1. Describe with diagrams and appropriate explanations the process of *electrolysis* as it applies to a solution of NaCl.

2. Define *oxidation* and *reduction* and state the part played by each in electrolysis.

3. State or write Faraday's three laws for electrolysis in your own words.

4. Describe or demonstrate a laboratory experiment which will show how Faraday's constant can be used to predict the mass deposited on an electrode in an electroplating process.

5. Apply *Faraday's law* for electrolysis to the solution of problems associated with electroplating operations.

6. Define a *primary cell* and give an example illustrating your knowledge of the anode material, the cathode material, and the electrolyte.

7. Explain what happens and give an example illustrating your knowledge of the anode material, the cathode material, and the electrolyte during the processes of charging and discharging a lead storage battery.

8. Define the *capacity rating* of a battery and apply it to problems involving the amperage delivered.

9. Illustrate with drawings and explanations the *Seebeck effect* and the *Peltier effect*.

DEFINITIONS

<u>Ions</u> - Particles which have an excess or deficiency of electrons.

<u>Electrolyte</u> - A substance which will conduct an electric current when it is dissolved in water or melted.

<u>Electrode</u> - A conducting element which emits or collects electrons or ions or controls their movement.

196

Anode - A positively charged electrode.

Cathode - A negatively charged electrode.

Electrolysis - A process by which chemical changes are brought about as the result of passing an electric current through a liquid.

Oxidation - A process by which particles lose electrons.

Reduction - A process by which particles gain electrons.

Faraday's first law - The mass of an element deposited at either electrode during electrolysis is directly proportional to the quantity of charge Q passed through the liquid.

Faraday's second law - The mass deposited during electrolysis is directly proportional to the atomic mass M of the plating materials.

Faraday's third law - The mass deposited during electrolysis is inversely proportional to the valence of the plating material.

Faraday's constant - The number of coulombs of charge which must be transferred through an electrolytic solution to liberate one kilomole of a plating material with a valence of 1.

Electrochemical cell - A source of emf which consists of two dissimilar metals immersed in an electrolytic solution.

Primary cell - A type of cell in which the chemical reactants must be replaced after a period of use.

Storage cell - A type of cell which is rechargeable by reversing the current through the cell.

Ampere-hour rating - The amount of current a battery can deliver in a specified length of time under specified conditions.

Thermoelectric effect - The reversible conversion of thermal energy into electric energy.

Thermocouple - An electrical junction formed by two dissimilar metals.

Seebeck effect - The conversion of heat energy into electric energy by means of a thermocouple.

Peltier effect - The conversion of electrical energy, supplied to a thermocouple, into heat energy.

PHYSICAL CONCEPTS

1. Faraday's laws can be used to calculate the mass deposited during an electroplating operation. The equation is

$$m = \frac{QM}{Fv} \qquad F = 9.65 \times 10^7 \text{ C/kmol} \qquad \text{Faraday's equation}$$

where Q = total charge transferred, C
M = atomic mass, kg
v = valence without regard to sign
m = mass deposited, kg
F = Faraday's constant, C/kmol

2. The capacity rating of a battery is expressed in ampere-hours (A·h) and is defined as

$$Life \text{ (h)} = \frac{Ampere\text{-}hour\ rating\ \textbf{(A·h)}}{Amperes\ delivered\ \textbf{(A)}}$$

TRUE-FALSE QUESTIONS

T F 1. The mass deposited during electrolysis is directly proportional to the valence of the plating material.

T F 2. The voltaic cell is an example of a primary electrolytic cell.

T F 3. When an electric current is passed through an electrolytic solution, oxidation occurs at the cathode.

T F 4. Faraday's constant represents the number of molecules in a mole of substance.

T F 5. The emf of a dry cell does not depend on the size of the cell but is determined by the nature of the reacting materials.

T F 6. A storage cell with an ampere-hour rating of 20 A·h will provide a current of 5 A for about 4 h.

T F 7. The Seebeck effect converts electric energy into thermal energy.

T F 8. When a lead storage cell is discharging, sulfuric acid is being removed from the solution and water is being added.

T F 9. The object to be plated during an electroplating process should be attached to the cathode.

T F 10. The mass of an element deposited at either electrode during a specified time interval is directly proportional to the electric current.

MULTIPLE-CHOICE QUESTIONS

1. The mass of an element deposited during electrolysis is inversely
   proportional to the
   (a) charge transferred
   (b) current
   (c) valence of the plating material
   (d) atomic mass of the plating material

2. Which of the following is not a primary cell?
   (a) lead-acid battery   (b) dry cell
   (c) voltaic cell   (d) a flashlight battery

3. A large dry cell and a small flashlight battery are compared.
   Which of the following is most likely to be true?
   (a) The emf of the large cell is greater.
   (b) The internal reactants are not the same.
   (c) The large is rechargeable, but the smaller is not.
   (d) The ampere-hour capacity is greater for the large cell.

4. When a current is supplied to a thermocouple, one junction
   becomes warmer than the other. This phenomenon is known as
   (a) the Seebeck effect   (b) the Peltier effect
   (c) Faraday's law   (d) the electrolytic effect

5. The emf of an electrolytic cell depends mostly on
   (a) the valence of the reacting materials
   (b) the quantity of electrolytic solution
   (c) the size of the electrodes
   (d) the density of the electrolytic solution

6. A battery has an ampere-hour capacity of 40 A·h. How long can
   a current of 8 A be maintained?
   (a) 0.2 h   (b) 5 h   (c) 10 h   (d) 320 h

7. A proper unit for Faraday's constant is
   (a) kg/mol   (b) C/kmol
   (c) kg/C   (d) molecules/kmol

8. In a laboratory, the apparatus consists of a copper sulfate
   solution ($CuSO_4$) containing two copper rods as electrodes. What
   current is required to plate 0.02 kg of copper in 2 h?
   (a) 8.33 A   (b) 10.4 A   (c) 12.33 A   (d) 15.67 A

9. A current of 20 A flows through a molten NaCl bath for 1 h.
   How much sodium is deposited at the cathode? (M = 22.91 for
   sodium)
   (a) 0.017 kg (b) 0.2 kg   (c) 0.34 kg   (d) 0.5 kg

10. What is the ampere-hour rating of a battery that can provide
    600 mA for 20 h?
    (a) 1.2 A·h   (b) 3 A·h   (c) 12 A·h   (d) 16 A·h

COMPLETION QUESTIONS

1. The mass deposited during electrolysis is inversely proportional to the _____ of the plating material. This is a statement of _____.

2. An _____ is a substance which, when dissolved in water or melted, will conduct an electric current.

3. A process of _____ causes particles to lose electrons, whereas _____ indicates a gain in electrons.

4. A valence larger than +1 for reactants in an electroplating process means that the same amount of charge will deposit _____ mass.

5. The transfer of 9.65 x 10^7 C of charge through an electrolytic solution will liberate _____ of a monovalent plating material. This number is known as _____ _____.

6. When a lead-acid battery is _____, the concentration of sulfuric acid is increasing.

7. An electrical junction formed by two dissimilar metals is a _____.

8. The amount of current a battery can deliver in a specified length of time for specified conditions is known as its _____.

9. The mass deposited during electrolysis is directly proportional to the _____ of the plating material and to the _____ passed through the electrolytic solution.

10. _____ is the process by which chemical changes are brought about as the result of passing an electric current through a liquid.

ANSWERS TO TRUE-FALSE, MULTIPLE CHOICE, AND COMPLETION QUESTIONS

1.	False	1.	c	1.	valence, Faraday's third law
2.	True	2.	a	2.	electrolyte
3.	True	3.	d	3.	oxidation, reduction
4.	False	4.	b	4.	a lesser
5.	True	5.	a	5.	1 kmol, Faraday's constant
6.	True	6.	b	6.	being charged
7.	False	7.	b	7.	thermocouple
8.	True	8.	a	8.	ampere-hour rating
9.	True	9.	a	9.	atomic mass M, quantity of charge
10.	True	10.	c	10.	electrolysis

CHAPTER 37. MAGNETISM AND THE MAGNETIC FIELD

CONTENTS

OBJECTIVES

You should be able to:

1. State or write the basic law of magnetic forces and demonstrate the law in a laboratory.

2. Explain *magnetic induction*, *retentivity*, and *magnetic saturation* in terms of the domain theory of magnetism.

3. Define *magnetic flux* and *magnetic flux density*, giving the units for each.

4. Define *permeability* and describe the part it plays in defining a relationship between magnetic field intensity and magnetic flux density.

5. Write and apply an equation relating the magnetic force on a moving charge to its velocity, its charge, and its direction in a field of known flux density.

6. Use the *right-hand-screw rule* in determining the direction of magnetic forces.

7. Determine the force on a current-carrying wire placed in a known B field.

8. Calculate the magnetic flux density (a) at a known distance from a current-carrying wire, (b) at the center of a current loop or coil, and (c) at the interior of a solenoid.

9. Define *relative permeability* and be able to use it in determining the flux density in magnetic media other than air.

10. Define *hysteresis* and explain the significance of the hysteresis loop for magnetic materials.

DEFINITIONS

Magnetism - The physical phenomenon associated with the attraction of certain metals and with nonelectrical forces on moving charges.

Magnetic poles - Regions near the ends of magnetized objects where the magnetic strength appears to be concentrated, e.g., north and south poles of a bar magnet.

Law of magnetic force - Like poles repel each other; unlike poles attract each other.

Coulomb's law for magnetic forces - The force of attraction or repulsion between two magnetic poles is directly proportional to the product of the pole strengths and inversely proportional to the square of their separation.

Magnetic domains - A theoretical microscopic region consisting of a group of atoms in a magnetic material.

Magnetic induction - Magnetization occurring as a result of the influence of a magnetizing force.

Retentivity - The ability of some magnetic materials to retain magnetism after the magnetizing force has been removed.

Magnetic saturation - The maximum magnetization which can occur for a given material. (All domains are aligned.)

Magnetic flux density - The number of magnetic flux lines which pass through a unit of area in a given region.

Weber - A unit of magnetic flux equivalent to one hundred million magnetic field lines.

Tesla - A unit of flux density equivalent to one weber per square meter.

Permeability - A measure of a material's ability to support magnetic flux lines.

Relative permeability - The ratio of the permeability of a material to that for a vacuum.

Diamagnetic - Materials with a relative permeability slightly less than unity. Such materials are feebly repelled by a strong magnet.

Paramagnetic - Materials with permeabilities slightly greater than that of a vacuum. Such materials are feebly attracted by a strong magnet.

Ferromagnetic - Magnetic materials having extremely high permeabilities. Such materials are strongly attracted by a magnet.

Right-hand-screw rule - The direction of the magnetic force on a
    moving charge is the same as the direction of advance of a
    right-hand screw if the velocity vector is rotated into the flux
    density vector.

Weber per square meter - A unit of flux density which produces a force
    of one newton on a charge of one coulomb moving perpendicular to
    the field with a velocity of one meter per second.

Hysteresis - The lagging of the magnetization behind the magnetizing
    force. The hysteresis loop is a measure of the energy lost during
    a magnetization cycle.

PHYSICAL CONCEPTS

1. The magnetic flux density B in a region of a magnetic field is
    the number of flux lines which pass through a unit of area
    perpendicular to the flux.

$$B = \frac{\phi}{A_\perp} = \frac{\phi}{A \sin \theta}$$ magnetic flux density

    where ϕ = flux, Wb
          A = unit area, m^2
          θ = angle that plane of area makes with flux
          B = magnetic flux density, T (1 T = 1 Wb/m^2)

2. The magnetic flux density B is proportional to the magnetic field
    intensity H. The constant of proportionality is the permeability
    of the medium in which the field exists.

$$B = \frac{\phi}{A_\perp} = \mu H$$ for a vacuum $\mu_0 = 4\pi \times 10^{-7}$ T·m/A

The *relative permeability* μ_r is the ratio of μ/μ_0. We can write

$$B = \mu_0 \mu_r H$$ where $\mu_r = \frac{\mu}{\mu_0}$ relative permeability

3. A magnetic field of flux density equal to one tesla will exert a
    force of one newton on a charge of one coulomb moving perpendicu-
    lar to the field with a velocity of one meter per second. The
    general case is described by Fig. 37-1 in which the charge moves
    at an angle θ with the field.

$$F = qvB \sin \theta \qquad B = \frac{F}{qv \sin \theta}$$ magnetic force on
a moving charge

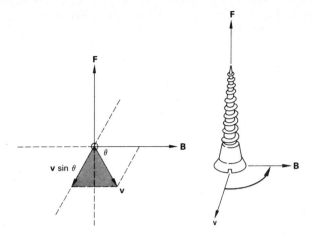

Fig. 37-1.

The direction of the magnetic force is given by the right-hand-screw rule, as illustrated in Fig. 37-1.

4. The force F on a wire carrying a current I at an angle θ with a flux density B is given by

$$\overline{F = BI l \sin \theta}$$ magnetic force on a conductor

where l is the length of the conductor.

5. Equations for many common magnetic fields are given below:

$$\overline{B = \frac{\mu I}{2 \pi d}}$$ long wire $$\overline{B = \frac{\mu I}{2r}}$$ center of loop

$$\overline{B = \frac{\mu N I}{2r}}$$ center of coil $$\overline{B = \frac{\mu N I}{L}}$$ solenoid

TRUE-FALSE QUESTIONS

T   F   1. Like magnetic poles repel each other whereas unlike magnetic poles attract each other.

T   F   2. Magnetic flux lines are drawn in such a way that the direction at any point is the same as the direction of the force exerted on a unit south pole placed at that point.

T   F   3. The weber is a unit of magnetic flux density.

T F 4. An electron projected from right to left through a magnetic field directed into the page will be deflected downward.

T F 5. The area of a hysteresis loop is a measure of flux density.

T F 6. The right-hand thumb rule can be used to determine the direction of a magnetic field surrounding a current-carrying conductor.

T F 7. Two current-carrying conductors placed near each other will experience a force of attraction if their currents are oppositely directed.

T F 8. The magnetic field lines for a solenoid are of the same shape as those for a bar magnet.

T F 9. A large hysteresis loop means a more efficient electromagnetic device.

T F 10. Magnetic materials having a high permeability will generally have a low retentivity.

MULTIPLE-CHOICE QUESTIONS

1. Which of the following is not a unit of magnetic induction of flux density?
   (a) weber per square meter   (b) gauss
   (c) tesla   (d) weber

2. Magnetic fields have no effect on
   (a) electric charges at rest
   (b) electric charges in motion
   (c) permanent magnets at rest
   (d) permanent magnets in motion

3. The magnetic flux density at a distance d from a long, current-carrying, straight wire is proportional to
   (a) d (b) $1/d$ (c) d^2 (d) $1/d^2$

4. Relative permeability is
   (a) the ratio of flux density in a material to that for a vacuum
   (b) very large for paramagnetic materials
   (c) small for ferromagnetic materials
   (d) equal to $4\pi \times 10^{-7}$ T·m/A for a vacuum

5. The current through a wire is directed into the page. If a magnetic field is directed from right to left, the force on the wire will be
   (a) to the right   (b) to the left
   (c) upward   (d) downward

6. An electron is projected from left to right into a flux density of 0.3 T directed into the paper. If the speed of the electron is 2 x 10^6 m/s, the magnetic force will be
   (a) 9.6 x 10^{-14} N   (b) 6.9 x 10^{-14} N
   (c) 5 x 10^{-13} N   (d) 4.8 x 10^{-14} N

7. A proton (+1.6 x 10^{-19} C) is projected from left to right at a velocity of 2 x 10^6 m/s. If an upward force of 1 x 10^{-13} N is observed, the magnetic flux density perpendicular to the velocity is approximately
   (a) 1.25 T out of the paper   (b) 1.25 T into the paper
   (c) 0.31 T out of the paper   (d) 0.31 T into the paper

8. A rectangular loop of wire 20 cm wide and 30 cm long makes an angle of 40° with a magnetic flux density of 0.3 T. The flux penetrating the loop is approximately
   (a) 0.01 Wb   (b) 0.02 Wb   (c) 2 Wb   (d) 115 Wb

9. The magnetic induction at a distance of 6 cm in air from a long current-carrying conductor is 12 x 10^{-6} T. The current in the wire is
   (a) 1.8 A   (b) 3.6 A   (c) 4.8 A   (d) 6.4 A

10. A solenoid has 60 turns of wire and a length of 16 cm and supports a current of 10 A. The relative permeability of the core is 1200. The magnetic induction at the center is approximately
    (a) 1.4 T   (b) 2.83 T   (c) 5.65 T   (d) 11 T

COMPLETION QUESTIONS

1. Hysteresis is the lagging of the _____ behind the _____ .

2. According to the right-hand thumb rule, if a current-carrying wire is grasped with the right hand so that the thumb points in the direction of the _____ , the curled fingers of that hand point in the direction of _____ .

3. A circular coil in the plane of the paper supports a clockwise electric current. The direction of the magnetic flux near the center is _____ .

4. The relative permeability of a material is the ratio of its _____ to that for a _____ .

5. _____ refers to the condition under which all the magnetic domains in a material are aligned.

6. The unit of flux density in the metric system of units is the _____ , and the unit of magnetic flux is the _____ .

7. In applying the right-hand-screw rule for magnetic effects on a conducting wire, the _____ is turned into the _____. The direction of the _____ will then be the same as the direction of advance of a right-hand screw.

8. A magnetic field having a flux density of one tesla will exert a force of one _____ on a charge of one _____ moving perpendicular to the field with a velocity of one _____.

9. Materials with a relative permeability slightly less than unity are said to be _____; _____ materials have permeabilities slightly greater than unity.

10. The ability of some materials to retain magnetism after the magnetizing force has been removed is referred to as _____.

ANSWERS TO TRUE-FALSE, MULTIPLE CHOICE, AND COMPLETION QUESTIONS

1. True	1. d	1. magnetization, magnetizing force
2. False	2. a	2. current, the magnetic field
3. False	3. b	3. into the paper
4. False	4. a	4. permeability, vacuum
5. False	5. c	5. magnetic saturation
6. True	6. a	6. tesla, weber
7. False	7. d	7. current vector, flux-density vector, magnetic force
8. True	8. a	8. newton, coulomb, meter per second
9. False	9. b	9. diamagnetic, paramagnetic
10. True	10. c	10. retentivity

CHAPTER 38.   FORCES AND TORQUES IN A MAGNETIC FIELD

CONTENTS

OBJECTIVES

You should be able to:

1. Determine the direction of the magnetic force on a current-carrying conductor in a known B field.

2. Calculate the magnetic torque on a coil of area A having N turns of wire carrying a current I when its orientation in a known B field is given.

3. Calculate the torque on a solenoid which is free to rotate in a known B field.

4. Disassemble a laboratory galvanometer and explain the function of each of the parts. If a galvanometer is not available, you should explain with drawings.

5. Explain with drawings how a galvanometer can be converted into a dc voltmeter and how it can be used as a dc ammeter.

6. Calculate for a galvanometer or a dc voltmeter of fixed sensitivity the multiplier resistance necessary to increase the range of the instrument to accommodate higher voltage.

7. Calculate the shunt resistance necessary to increase the range of a galvanometer or an ammeter of fixed sensitivity.

8. Disassemble a laboratory dc motor and explain the function of each of its parts, with particular emphasis on the *split-ring commutator*; if a motor is not available, explain with drawings.

DEFINITIONS

Magnetic torque - The torque experienced by a current element in a magnetic field.

Galvanometer - An electromagnetic device utilized for the detection of an electric current.

Voltmeter - A galvanometer which is calibrated to measure voltage. The range is determined by the *multiplier resistance* in series with the galvanometer.

Ammeter - A galvanometer which is calibrated to measure electric current. The range is determined by a *shunt resistance* connected in parallel with the galvanometer.

Motor - An electromagnetic device which converts electric energy into mechanical, rotational energy in the form of magnetic torque.

Armature - The central element of a motor, consisting of the core and a number of coils of wire.

Split-ring commutator - Two metal half rings fused to each end of the conducting loop in a simple dc motor. It is this element which accomplishes the current reversals necessary for continuous rotation of the loop.

PHYSICAL CONCEPTS

1. The magnetic torque on a current-carrying coil of wire having N turns of wire is given by

$$L = NBIA \cos \theta \qquad \text{magnetic torque}$$

   where N = number of turns of wire
   B = flux density, T
   I = current, A
   A = area of the coil of wire, m^2
   α = angle plane of coil makes with field

2. The same equation applies for a solenoid, except that the angle α is generally replaced with θ, the angle the solenoid axis makes with the field.

$$L = NBIA \sin \theta \qquad \text{torque on a solenoid}$$

3. The multiplier resistance R_m which must be placed in series with a voltmeter to give full-scale deflection for V_B is found from

$$R_m = \frac{V_B - I_g R_g}{I_g} \qquad \text{multiplier resistance}$$

   I_g is the galvanometer current, and R_g is its resistance.

4. The shunt resistance R_s which must be placed in parallel with an ammeter to give full-scale deflection for a current I is

$$R_s = \frac{I_g R_g}{I - I_g} \qquad \text{shunt resistance}$$

TRUE-FALSE QUESTIONS

T   F   1.   The sensitivity of a galvanometer is determined entirely
             by its electrical resistance.

T   F   2.   A horizontal current loop which is parallel with a mag-
             netic field directed from right to left will experience
             a counterclockwise torque if the loop current is
             counterclockwise when viewed from the top.

T   F   3.   The magnetic torque on a current loop is a maximum when
             the angle between the plane of the loop and the magnetic
             field is 90°.

T   F   4.   The equation for computing the magnetic torque on a
             current loop of N turns can also be used for a solenoid
             of N turns.

T   F   5.   The radical magnetic field for a galvanometer helps to
             ensure that the pointer deflection will be directly
             proportional to the current in the coil.

T   F   6.   Placing a low-resistance wire across the terminals of an
             ammeter will decrease the range of currents which can be
             measured.

T   F   7.   Increasing the multiplier resistance for a voltmeter will
             increase the range of the voltmeter.

T   F   8.   Voltmeters must be connected in parallel because of the
             low multiplier resistance which would short the circuit
             if it were placed in series.

T   F   9.   The proper insertion of an ammeter or a voltmeter into a
             circuit will alter the current in that circuit slightly,
             introducing some error.

T   F   10. The torque output by a simple dc motor is not uniform.

MULTIPLE-CHOICE QUESTIONS

1. The torque on a solenoid in a magnetic field is not a function of
   its
   (a) loop area   (b) number of loops
   (c) length   (d) current

2. Which of the following must be a high-resistance instrument?
   (a) voltmeter   (b) ammeter   (c) motor   (d) galvanometer

3. The minimum range of a given ammeter is determined by the
   (a) value of the shunt resistance
   (b) value of the multiplier resistance
   (c) load resistance
   (d) resistance and spring tension in the galvanometer element

4. The torque on a current-carrying loop is a maximum when the plane of the loop
(a) is parallel with the magnetic field
(b) is perpendicular to the magnetic field
(c) is at an angle of 45° with the magnetic field
(d) none of the above

5. The range of a dc voltmeter can be increased by
(a) increasing the circuit load resistance
(b) increasing the multiplier resistance
(c) decreasing the multiplier resistance
(d) placing a shunt resistance across the voltmeter terminals

6. A galvanometer has an internal resistance of 0.2 Ω and gives a full-scale deflection for a current of 3 mA. What multiplier resistance is required to convert this instrument into a voltmeter whose maximum range is 200 V?
(a) 66 Ω (b) 33 Ω
(c) 3.3×10^4 Ω (d) 6.67×10^4 Ω

7. If the galvanometer in the problem above is used to construct an ammeter whose maximum range is 20 A, what shunt resistance must be added?
(a) 1×10^{-5} Ω (b) 3×10^{-5} Ω
(c) 5×10^{-5} Ω (d) 7×10^{-5} Ω

8. A rectangular coil of wire has a width of 12 cm and a length of 20 cm. The coil is mounted in a uniform magnetic field of flux density 4×10^{-3} T, and a current of 20 A is sent through the windings. If the coil makes an angle of 30° with the field, how many turns of wire will be required to produce an output torque of 0.5 N·m?
(a) 100 turns   (b) 200 turns   (c) 300 turns   (d) 400 turns

9. A commercial 5-V voltmeter requires a current of 10 mA to produce full-scale deflection. It can be converted into an instrument with a range of 50 V by adding a multiplier resistance of
(a) 9000 Ω (b) 4500 Ω (c) 2250 Ω (d) 1125 Ω

10. A laboratory ammeter has a resistance of 0.1 Ω and reads 3 A full scale. The shunt resistance which must be added to increase the range of the ammeter tenfold is
(a) 0.0111 Ω (b) 0.0011 Ω (c) 0.022 Ω (d) 0.0022 Ω

COMPLETION QUESTIONS

1. The magnetic torque on a current-carrying loop of wire is directly proportional to the _____ of the magnetic field, the _____ of the loop, the _____ in the loop, and the _____ of the angle between the plane of the loop and the magnetic field.

2. When the plane of the loop is perpendicular to the field, the resultant torque on the loop when it supports a current is _____.

3. Any device used for the detection of an electric current is called a _____.

4. A voltmeter can be constructed by placing a _____ resistance in series with a _____.

5. An ammeter is designed by placing a _____ resistance in _____ with a _____.

6. The current reversals required for continuous rotation of the armature in a dc motor are accomplished by using a _____.

7. A galvanometer can be used to measure both _____ and _____.

8. An ideal ammeter has a _____ resistance whereas the ideal voltmeter has a _____ resistance.

9. Three essential parts of a galvanometer are a _____, a _____, and a _____.

10. When inserting a voltmeter into a circuit, it must be connected in _____. An ammeter is connected in _____.

ANSWERS TO TRUE-FALSE, MULTIPLE CHOICE, AND COMPLETION QUESTIONS

1.	False	1.	c	1.	flux density, area, current, cosine
2.	True	2.	a	2.	zero
3.	False	3.	d	3.	galvanometer
4.	True	4.	a	4.	multiplier, galvanometer
5.	True	5.	b	5.	shunt, parallel, galvanometer
6.	False	6.	d	6.	commutator
7.	True	7.	b	7.	current, voltage
8.	False	8.	c	8.	low, high
9.	True	9.	b	9.	magnet, coil, pointer
10.	True	10.	a	10.	parallel, series

CHAPTER 39. ELECTROMAGNETIC INDUCTION

CONTENTS

OBJECTIVES

You should be able to:

1. Write a quantitative relationship for computing the *induced emf* in a coil of N turns and apply it in the solution of electromagnetic problems.

2. Describe or demonstrate in the laboratory two principal ways in which *magnetic flux* can change.

3. Write a quantitative relationship for computing the induced emf in a length of wire moving with a velocity v directed at an angle θ in a known B field and apply the relationship to the solution of electromagnetic problems.

4. State or write *Lenz's law* and use it to determine the direction of induced emf or current.

5. Describe the function of each of the parts of an ac generator or a dc generator in the laboratory; if the generators are not available, explain with drawings.

6. Calculate the instantaneous and maximum emf or current generated by a simple ac generator.

7. Explain or demonstrate how *back emf* reduces the *net* voltage delivered by a generator.

8. Demonstrate with the use of diagrams your knowledge of *series-wound* and *shunt-wound* motors and solve for starting current and operating voltage in problems relating to each type of motor.

9. Diagram the operation of a *transformer* and write an equation relating input and output voltages to primary and secondary turns.

10. Define the *efficiency* of a transformer and write and apply an equation showing the inverse relationship between induced current and induced voltage.

DEFINITIONS

<u>Induced voltage</u> - The voltage or emf produced in a conductor when relative motion exists between the conductor and a magnetic field.

<u>Lenz's law</u> - Whenever an emf is induced, the induced current must be in such a direction as will oppose the change by which the current is induced.

<u>Generator</u> - A rotating machine which converts mechanical energy into electric energy.

<u>Back emf</u> - The opposing or counter emf induced in a motor as a result of the rotational motion of the armature windings relative to the magnetic field.

<u>Series-wound motor</u> - A motor in which the field and armature circuits are connected in series; sometimes referred to as a *universal* motor.

<u>Shunt-wound motor</u> - A dc motor in which the field circuit and the armature circuit are connected in parallel. The speed can be controlled by varying the voltage applied to either the armature or the field.

<u>Compound-wound motor</u> - A dc motor having two separate field windings. One, usually the predominant field, is connected in parallel with the armature circuit, and the other is connected in series.

<u>Transformer</u> - An electrical device which uses electromagnetic induction to transform electric energy from one or more circuits into electric energy in one or more other circuits at a different voltage and current.

PHYSICAL CONCEPTS

1. A magnetic flux changing at the rate of 1 Wb/s will induce an emf of 1 V for each turn of a conductor. Symbolically,

$$E = -N\frac{\Delta\phi}{\Delta t} \qquad \text{induced emf}$$

Two principal ways in which the flux changes are

$$\Delta\phi = \Delta B\ A \qquad \Delta\phi = B\ \Delta A$$

2. The induced emf due to a wire of length l moving with a velocity v at an angle θ with a field B is given by

$$E = Blv\ \sin\theta \qquad \text{emf due to moving wire}$$

3. According to *Lenz's law*, the induced current must be in such a direction that it produces a magnetic force which opposes the force causing the motion.

4. The instantaneous emf generated by a coil of N turns moving with an angular velocity ω or frequency f is

$$E_{inst} = NBA\omega \sin \omega t \qquad E_{inst} = 2\pi f NBA \sin 2\pi f t$$

The maximum emf occurs when the sin is zero. Thus

$$E_{max} = NBA\omega \qquad E_{max} = E_{max} \sin 2\pi f t$$

5. Since the induced current is proportional to E, we also have

$$i_{inst} = i_{max} \sin 2\pi f t \qquad \text{instantaneous current}$$

6. The back emf in a motor is the induced voltage which causes a reduction in the net voltage delivered to a circuit.

   Applied voltage - induced back emf = net voltage

$$V - E_b = IR \qquad E_b = V - IR$$

7. For a transformer having N_p primary and N_s secondary turns

$$\frac{Primary\ voltage}{Secondary\ voltage} = \frac{primary\ turns}{secondary\ turns} \qquad \frac{E_p}{E_s} = \frac{N_p}{N_s}$$

8. The efficiency of a transformer is

$$E = \frac{\text{power output}}{\text{power input}} = \frac{E_p i_p}{E_s i_s} \qquad \text{transformer efficiency}$$

TRUE-FALSE QUESTIONS

T   F   1. Lenz's law is a consequence of the fact that energy must be conserved.

T   F   2. The magnitude of an induced emf is directly proportional to the rate at which magnetic flux lines are cut by a conductor.

T   F   3. A generator is a device which converts magnetic energy into electric energy.

T F   4. A transformer can only be used for alternating current.

T F   5. The back emf in the armature of an electric motor is zero when the motor is started and rises as the motor's speed increases.

T F   6. If the armature of a generator is rotating with a constant angular velocity in a constant magnetic field, the induced emf will also be constant.

T F   7. For an ac generator, the maximum current occurs when the induced emf is a minimum.

T F   8. Every motor is also a generator.

T F   9. In a shunt-wound motor, the output speed can be controlled by varying the input current to either the field windings or the armature windings.

T F 10. A series-wound motor is preferable if a large starting torque is desirable.

MULTIPLE-CHOICE QUESTIONS

1. When a wire moves perpendicular to a magnetic field, the induced emf does not depend on
   (a) the velocity of the wire
   (b) the resistance of the wire
   (c) the flux density of the magnetic field
   (d) the orientation of the wire

2. A wire parallel to the paper moves downward into a flux density directed into the paper. The induced current
   (a) will be directed to the left
   (b) will be zero because the motion is perpendicular to the field
   (c) will be directed to the right
   (d) will be opposite to the induced emf, according to Lenz's law

3. Which of the following is *not* a component of a simple ac generator?
   (a) field magnet   (b) split-ring commutator
   (c) armature   (d) brushes

4. The instantaneous emf produced by a simple ac generator is a maximum when the angular displacement of the loop is
   (a) an integral multiple of $\pi/2$
   (b) an odd multiple of $\pi/2$
   (c) an even multiple of π
   (d) an odd multiple of π

5. The ratio of the primary voltage to the secondary voltage for a transformer does *not* depend on
   (a) the relative number of turns in the windings
   (b) the permeability of the core
   (c) the primary voltage
   (d) the resistance in the windings

6. A coil of wire of area 0.3 m^2 has 90 turns of wire and is suspended with its plane perpendicular to a uniform magnetic field. An emf of -2 V is induced when the coil is flipped parallel to the field in 0.4 s. The flux density of the field is approximately
   (a) 0.01 T   (b) 0.02 T   (c) 0.03 T   (d) 0.04 T

7. An armature in an ac generator consists of 600 turns, each having an area of 0.4 m^2. The coil rotates in a field of flux density 2 x 10^{-3} T. What must the rotational frequency of the armature be in order to induce a maximum emf of 12 V?
   (a) 200 rpm   (b) 226 rpm   (c) 239 rpm   (d) 478 rpm

8. A wire 0.2 cm long moves at a constant speed of 5 m/s in a direction that is 37° with respect to a magnetic field of 0.2 T directed perpendicular to the wire. The induced emf is approximately
   (a) 0.12 V   (b) 0.16 V   (c) 0.20 V   (d) 0.24 V

9. A 120-V shunt motor has a field resistance of 200 Ω and an armature resistance of 12 Ω. At full speed, the back emf of the motor is 90 V. The operating current is approximately
   (a) 3 A   (b) 6 A   (c) 12 A   (d) 16 A

10. A transformer has 400 secondary turns and only 50 primary turns. If an ac voltage of 120 V is connected to the primary coil, the output voltage is
    (a) 15 V   (b) 240 V   (c) 430 V   (d) 960 V

COMPLETION QUESTIONS

1. A magnetic flux changing at the rate of one _____ will induce an emf of one _____ for each _____ of the conductor.

2. Whenever an electric current is induced, its direction must be such that it produces a _____ which opposes the _____ causing the motion. This is a consequence of _____.

3. For a dc motor in operation, the net voltage delivered to the armature coils is equal to the _____ less the _____.

4. The major components of a simple ac generator are the _____ _____, the _____, and _____ with _____.

5. Three types of motors discussed in this text are the _____ _____, the _____ and the _____.

6. The current drawn by an electric motor is a maximum when the motor is _____.

7. In an ideal transformer, the power output is equal to the _____.

8. In a step-down transformer, the number of turns in the secondary coil must be _____ the number of turns in the primary coil.

9. A simple transformer consists of three essential parts: (a) _____, (b) _____, and (c) _____.

10. In a _____, the field windings and the armature windings are connected in parallel.

ANSWERS TO TRUE-FALSE, MULTIPLE CHOICE, AND COMPLETION QUESTIONS

1.	True	1.	b	1.	weber per second, volt, turn
2.	True	2.	c	2.	magnetic force, force, Lenz's law
3.	False	3.	b		
4.	True	4.	b	3.	applied voltage, back emf
5.	True	5.	c	4.	field magnets, armature, slip rings, brushes
6.	False	6.	c		
7.	False	7.	c	5.	series-wound motor, shunt motor, compound motor
8.	True	8.	a		
9.	True	9.	a	6.	starting
10.	True	10.	d	7.	power input
				8.	less than
				9.	primary coil, secondary coil, a soft-iron core
				10.	shunt-wound motor

CHAPTER 40. ALTERNATING-CURRENT CIRCUITS

CONTENTS

OBJECTIVES

You should be able to:

1. Solve for the instantaneous charge and for the instantaneous current in the charging or discharging of a capacitor.

2. Solve for the instantaneous current in an *inductor* during its growth and decay.

3. State the practical value of the *time constant* as it applies to an inductor or to a capacitor and calculate the time constant in specific problems.

4. Define *inductance* and describe the effect it has on an electric current.

5. Define and be able to compute the effective values of voltage and current as they apply to ac circuits.

6. Explain with diagrams the phase relationships for a circuit with (a) pure resistance, (b) pure capacitance, and (c) pure inductance.

7. Write and apply relationships for the computation of *capacitive* and *inductive reactance*.

8. Calculate the *impedance*, the *phase angle*, and the *effective current* for a series ac circuit containing resistance, capacitance, and inductance.

9. Demonstrate by definition and example your understanding of *electrical resonance*.

10. Calculate the resonant frequency of the circuit when the inductance and capacitance in an ac circuit are given.

11. Define *power factor* and solve for it in a given ac circuit.

DEFINITIONS

Capacitor - An electrostatic device which has a capability of storing charge. It regulates and controls the flow of charge in an ac circuit.

Inductor - An element of an ac circuit which consists of a continuous loop or coil of wire. A self-induced emf opposes increases or decreases in the circuit current.

Henry - A unit of inductance which will induce an emf of one volt when the current is changing at the rate of one ampere per second.

Inductance - The property of an ac circuit which opposes any change in the amount of current flowing in the circuit.

Reactance - The nonresistive opposition to the flow of an alternating current. If it is caused by an inductor, it is called inductive reactance, and if it is caused by capacitance, it is called capacitive reactance.

Impedance - The combined opposition that a circuit offers to the flow of alternating current. It includes the effects of capacitance, inductance, and resistance.

Phase diagram - A vectoral representation of the relationships of resistive, capacitive, and inductive parameters in an ac circuit.

Phase angle - An angle on the phase diagram which indicates how much voltage leads or lags the current in an ac circuit. It is equal to the angle whose tangent is the ratio of the net reactance in a circuit to its resistance.

Resonant frequency - The frequency for which the capacitive reactance in an ac circuit is exactly equal to its inductive reactance, resulting in a maximum current that is in phase.

Power factor - A measure of the effective power consumed by an ac circuit. It is equal to the cosine of the phase angle.

Effective current - That alternating current which will develop the same power as a direct current of the same value.

Effective voltage - The ratio of effective current to the impedance in an ac circuit.

PHYSICAL CONCEPTS

1. When a capacitor is being charged, the instantaneous values of the charge Q and the current i are found from

$$Q = CV_B(1 - e^{-t/RC}) \qquad i = \frac{V_B}{R}e^{-t/RC}$$

220

The charge on the capacitor will rise to 63 percent of its maxi-
mum value as the current delivered to the capacitor decreases to
37 percent of its initial value during a period of one time
constant τ.

$$\tau = RC$$ time constant

2. When a capacitor is discharging, the instantaneous values of the charge and current are given by

$$Q = CV_B e^{-t/RC}$$ $$i = \frac{-V_B}{R} e^{-t/RC}$$

Both the charge and the current decay to 37 percent of their initial values after discharging for one time constant.

3. When alternating current passes through a coil of wire, an inductor, a self-induced emf arises to oppose the change. This emf is given by

$$E = -L\frac{\Delta i}{\Delta t}$$ $$L = -\frac{E}{\Delta i/\Delta t}$$

This constant L is called the inductance. An inductance of one henry (H) exists if an emf of one volt is induced by a current changing at the rate of one ampere per second.

4. The rise and decay of current in an inductor are found from

$$i = \frac{V_B}{R}(1 - e^{-(R/L)t})$$ current rise

$$i = \frac{V_B}{R} e^{-(R/L)t}$$ current decay

In an inductive circuit, the current will rise to 63 percent of its maximum value or decay to 37 percent of its maximum in a period of one time constant. For an inductor, the time constant is

$$\tau = \frac{L}{R}$$ time constant

5. Since alternating currents and voltages vary continuously, we speak of an effective ampere and an effective volt that are defined in terms of their maximum values as follows:

$$i_{eff} = 0.707 i_{max}$$ $$E_{eff} = 0.707 E_{max}$$

6. Both capacitors and inductors offer resistance to the flow of alternating current (called reactance), calculated from

$$X_L = 2\pi f L \qquad \Omega \qquad \text{inductive reactance } X_L$$

$$X_C = \frac{1}{2\pi f C} \qquad \Omega \qquad \text{capacitive reactance } X_C$$

The symbol f refers to the frequency of the alternating current in hertz. One hertz is one cycle per second.

7. The voltage, current, and resistance in a series ac circuit are studied with the use of phasor diagrams. Figure 40-1 illustrates such a diagram for X_C, X_L, and R. The resultant of these vectors is the effective resistance of the entire circuit called the *impedance* Z. From the figure

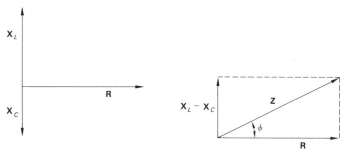

Fig. 40-1. Impedance diagram.

$$Z = \sqrt{R^2 + (X_L - X_C)^2} \qquad \Omega \qquad \text{impedance}$$

8. If we apply Ohm's law to each part of the circuit and then to the entire circuit, we obtain the following useful equations. First, the total voltage is given by

$$V = \sqrt{V_R^2 + (V_L - V_C)^2} \qquad\qquad \text{voltage}$$

$$V_R = iR \qquad V_L = iX_L \qquad V_C = iX_C \qquad V = iZ$$

$$V = i\sqrt{R^2 + (X_L - X_C)^2} \qquad \text{Ohm's law}$$

9. Because the voltage leads the current in an inductive circuit and lags the current in a capacitive circuit, the voltage and current maxima and minima usually do not coincide. The phase angle ϕ is given by

$$\tan \phi = \frac{V_L - V_C}{V_B} \qquad \text{or} \qquad \tan \phi = \frac{X_L - X_C}{R}$$

10. The resonant frequency occurs when the net reactance is zero ($X_L = X_C$):

$$f_r = \frac{1}{2\pi\sqrt{LC}} \qquad \text{resonant frequency}$$

11. No power is consumed because of capacitance or inductance. Since power is a function of the component of the impedance along the resistance axis, we can write

$$P = iV \cos \phi \qquad \text{power factor} = \cos \phi$$

$$\cos \phi = \frac{R}{Z} \qquad \cos \phi = \frac{R}{\sqrt{R^2 + (X_L - X_C)^2}}$$

TRUE-FALSE QUESTIONS

T F 1. In a capacitive circuit, the current delivered to a capacitor will rise to 63 percent of its maximum value after charging for a period of one time constant.

T F 2. In an inductive circuit, the current decays to 37 percent of its initial value in a period of one time constant.

T F 3. A capacitor with a breakdown voltage of 150 V would be safe to use in an ac circuit if the ac voltage is only 120 V.

T F 4. Capacitive reactance and inductive reactance increase with an increase in frequency of an alternating current.

T F 5. The effective voltage V in a series ac circuit can be defined as the algebraic sum of V_C, V_L, and V_R.

T F 6. The power factor in an ac circuit is the ratio of its resistance to its impedance.

T F 7. Under a condition of resonance in an ac circuit, the current will be in phase with the voltage.

T F 8. Reactance, impedance, and resistance are all measured in the same physical unit (ohms).

T F 9. In a circuit containing pure capacitance, the voltage leads the current by 90°.

223

T   F   10.   A negative phase angle occurs when the current leads the voltage in an ac circuit.

MULTIPLE-CHOICE QUESTIONS

1. The voltage of a circuit containing only inductive reactance
   (a) is in phase with the current
   (b) leads the current by 90°
   (c) lags the current by 90°
   (d) leads the current by less than 90°

2. An alternating voltage has a maximum value of 30 V. The effective value is approximately
   (a) 15 V   (b) 21.2 V   (c) 30 V   (d) 42.9 V

3. As the capacitance in an ac circuit increases, the resonant frequency
   (a) increases   (b) decreases
   (c) remains the same   (d) approaches zero

4. The ratio of the pure resistance in an ac circuit to the impedance is known as
   (a) the power factor   (b) the phase angle
   (c) the resonant frequency   (d) the net reactance

5. In a circuit containing pure capacitance, during a period of one time constant,
   (a) the charge decays to 63 percent of its initial value
   (b) the charge increases to 37 percent of its initial value
   (c) the current decays to 37 percent of its initial value
   (d) the capacitor is completely charged

6. In an ac circuit containing a coil with an inductance of 0.3 H, the voltage is 120 V at 60 Hz. Neglecting resistance, the effective current in the coil is
   (a) 0.27 A   (b) 0.53 A   (c) 1.06 A   (d) 2.12 A

7. A 50-Ω resistor, a 0.5-H inductor, and a 12-μF capacitor are connected in series with a 120-V, 60-Hz alternating current. The effective current is approximately
   (a) 2 A   (b) 4 A   (c) 6 A   (d) 8 A

8. In the above problem, the power factor is
   (a) 0.66   (b) 0.72   (c) 0.83   (d) 0.92

9. An 800-Ω resistor, a 0.6-H inductor, and a 4-μF capacitor are connected in series with a 220-V, 50-Hz source of alternating current. The phase angle is approximately
   (a) -31°   (b) -37°   (c) 31°   (d) 37°

224

10. A circuit contains a 12-μF capacitor, a 40-Ω resistor, a switch, and a 20-V dc battery connected in series. After the switch is closed, the capacitor can be considered fully charged after a time of
(a) 0.00048 s   (b) 0.0012 s   (c) 0.0024 s   (d) 0.0048 s

COMPLETION QUESTIONS

1. One effective ampere is that alternating current which will develop the same _____ as _____ of direct current.

2. In an _____ circuit, the current decays to 37 percent of its initial value in a period equal to one _____.

3. In a capacitive circuit, the _____ leads the _____ and the phase angle is _____.

4. For an ac circuit containing capacitance, inductance, and resistance, the current will be a maximum when the frequency of the alternating voltage is equal to _____.

5. The power factor is equal to the _____ of the circuit divided by the _____.

6. When the voltage and current reach maximum and minimum values at the same time, they are said to be _____.

7. A given inductor has an inductance of one _____ if an emf of one _____ is induced by a current changing at the rate of one _____.

8. In an inductive circuit, an increase in frequency of the applied voltage will _____ the effective current.

9. At resonant frequency, an ac circuit containing resistance, inductance, and capacitance acts as if it contained only _____.

10. A household ac circuit has a 110-V 60-Hz source of current. The actual voltage varies from _____ to _____.

ANSWERS TO TRUE-FALSE, MULTIPLE CHOICE, AND COMPLETION QUESTIONS

1.	False	1.	b	1.	power, one ampere
2.	True	2.	b	2.	inductive, time constant
3.	False	3.	b	3.	current, voltage, negative
4.	False	4.	a	4.	the resonant frequency
5.	False	5.	c	5.	resistance, impedance
6.	True	6.	c	6.	in phase

ANSWERS (Continued)

7.	True	7.	a	7.	henry, volt, ampere per second
8.	True	8.	c	8.	decrease
9.	False	9.	b	9.	resistance
10.	True	10.	c	10.	- 155, +155 V

CHAPTER 41. MODERN PHYSICS AND THE ATOM

CONTENTS

OBJECTIVES

You should be able to:

1. State Einstein's first and second postulates and give examples
   to illustrate your understanding of these concepts.

2. Calculate relativistic changes in length, mass, and time
   intervals according to Einstein's equations.

3. Demonstrate your understanding of the equivalence of mass and
   energy by converting from mass units to energy units and vice
   versa.

4. Write and apply physical relationships for the total energy and
   for the kinetic energy of a particle moving with relativistic
   speed.

5. Predict the maximum kinetic energy of a photoelectron when the
   threshold frequency and the frequency of incident light are given.

6. Write and apply a physical relationship for calculating the
   de Broglie wavelength of a particle.

7. Describe with appropriate diagrams the contributions of Rutherford
   and Bohr to our understanding of the atom.

8. Sketch on a single diagram the Balmer, Lyman, and Pashen spectral
   series.

9. Demonstrate with appropriate figures an understanding of emission
   and absorption spectra.

10. Write Bohr's first postulate and use the concept of de Broglie
    standing waves to verify it.

11. Write and illustrate the meaning of Bohr's second postulate.

12. Calculate the energy emitted or absorbed by the hydrogen atom when
    the electron moves to a lower or higher energy level.

DEFINITIONS

Relativistic mass - The mass of an object which takes into account the increase in mass due to relative motion.

Relativistic contraction - The decrease in length which is due to relative motion between an observer and the object being measured.

Time dilation - A term which refers to the fact that a clock moving with respect to an observer ticks less rapidly, i.e., records longer time intervals, than to a person traveling with the clock.

Einstein's first postulate - The laws of physics are the same for all frames of reference moving with a constant velocity with respect to each other.

Einstein's second postulate - The free-space velocity of light is constant for all observers, independent of their state of motion.

Work function - The minimum energy required to eject a photoelectron from a surface.

Threshold frequency - The lowest frequency of an incident photon which can cause an electron to leave a surface.

De Broglie wavelength - The wavelength of a particle which is equal to the ratio of Planck's constant to the momentum of the particle.

Line emission spectrum - A spectrum formed by the dispersion of light emitted from an excited gas. It consists of bright lines which correspond to characteristic wavelengths.

Line absorption spectrum - A continuous spectrum interrupted by dark lines or bands at points where absorbed wavelengths would normally occur.

Bohr's first postulate - An electron can exist only in orbits where its angular momentum is an integral multiple of $h/2\pi$.

Bohr's second postulate - If an electron changes from one stable orbit to any other, it loses or gains energy in discrete quanta equal to the difference in energy between the initial and final states.

Principal quantum number - A positive integer used to describe the possible energy levels for an atomic electron.

PHYSICAL CONCEPTS

1. According to Einstein's equations of relativity, length, mass, and time are affected by relativistic speeds. The changes become more significant as the ratio of an object's velocity v to the free-space velocity of light c becomes larger.

$$L = L_0 \sqrt{1 - \frac{v^2}{c^2}}$$ relativistic contraction

$$m = \frac{m_0}{\sqrt{1 - v^2/c^2}}$$ relativistic mass

$$t = \frac{t_0}{\sqrt{1 - v^2/c^2}}$$ time dilation

In the above equations, $c = 3 \times 10^8$ m/s.

2. The total energy of a particle of rest mass m_0 and speed v can be written in either of the following forms:

$$E = mc^2 \qquad E = \sqrt{m_0^2 c^4 + p^2 c^2}$$ total energy

In these equations m is the relativistic mass as determined by the speed v, and p is the momentum mv.

The *relativistic kinetic energy* is found from

$$E_K = (m - m_0)c^2$$ relativistic kinetic energy

3. The quantum theory of electromagnetic radiation relates the energy of such radiation to its frequency f or wavelength λ.

$$E = hf \qquad E = \frac{hc}{\lambda} \qquad h = 6.63 \times 10^{-34} \text{ J/Hz}$$

4. In the photoelectric effect, the kinetic energy of the ejected electrons is the energy of the incident radiation hf less the work function of the surface W.

$$E_K = \tfrac{1}{2}mv^2 = hf - W$$ photoelectric equation

The lowest frequency f_0 at which a photoelectron is ejected is the threshold frequency. It corresponds to the work-function energy W.

$$f_0 = \frac{W}{h} \qquad W = hf_0$$ threshold frequency

5. By combining wave theory with particle theory, de Broglie was able to give the following equation for the wavelength of any particle whose mass and velocity are known:

$$\lambda = \frac{h}{mv} \qquad h = 6.63 \times 10^{-34} \text{ J/Hz} \qquad \text{de Broglie wavelength}$$

6. Bohr's first postulate states that the angular momentum of an electron in any orbit must be a multiple of $h/2\pi$. His second postulate states that the energy absorbed or emitted by an atom is in discrete amounts equal to the difference in energy levels of an electron. These concepts are given as equations below:

$$mvr = \frac{nh}{2\pi} \qquad hf = E_f - E_i \qquad \text{Bohr's postulates}$$

7. Absorption and emission spectra for gases verify the discrete nature of radiation. The wavelength λ or frequency f which corresponds to a change in electron energy levels is given by

$$\frac{1}{\lambda} = R\left(\frac{1}{n_f^2} - \frac{1}{n_i^2}\right) \qquad f = Rc\left(\frac{1}{n_f^2} - \frac{1}{n_0^2}\right)$$

$$R = \frac{me^4}{8\varepsilon_0^2\, hc} = 1.097 \times 10^7 \text{ m}^{-1} \qquad \text{Rydberg's constant}$$

8. The total energy of a particular quantum state n for the hydrogen atom is given by:

$$E_n = - \frac{me^4}{8\varepsilon_0^2 n^2 h^2} \qquad \text{or} \qquad E_n = - \frac{13.6 \text{ eV}}{n^2}$$

where $\varepsilon_0 = 8.85 \times 10^{-12} \text{ C}^2/\text{N·m}^2$
$e = 1.6 \times 10^{-19} \text{ C}$
$m_e = 9.1 \times 10^{-31} \text{ kg}$
$h = 6.63 \times 10^{-34} \text{ J/Hz}$

TRUE-FALSE QUESTIONS

T F 1. When two rocket ships A and B move toward each other at uniform speed, it is not possible for the astronauts on either ship to determine whether (a) ship A is moving and ship B is at rest, (b) ship B is moving and ship A is at rest, or (c) both ships are moving.

T F 2. Einstein's second postulate tells us that the velocity of light is always constant.

T F 3. The kinetic energy of a particle traveling at relativistic speeds is equal to the difference between its total energy and its rest mass energy.

T F 4. In the photoelectric effect a surface with a large work function is likely to produce photoelectrons with higher kinetic energy.

T F 5. De Broglie wavelengths can be calculated only for charged particles such as protons and electrons.

T F 6. The wavelengths from an emission spectrum of an element should not be expected to coincide with the wavelengths determined from an absorption spectrum of that element.

T F 7. The Balmer spectral series in an emission spectrum results from electrons in higher energy levels dropping to the ground state for the hydrogen atom.

T F 8. The stable electron orbits are those which contain an integral number of de Broglie wavelengths.

T F 9. The energy of an electron in the first excited state is 4 times its energy in the ground state.

T F 10. Rutherford's work with the scattering of alpha particles resulted in a nuclear theory of matter.

MULTIPLE-CHOICE QUESTIONS

1. According to the modern theory of relativity, newtonian mechanics is
   (a) totally incorrect
   (b) approximately correct for any velocity
   (c) approximately correct for speeds much less than the speed of light
   (d) correct for all velocities

2. A clock of mass m and length L records a time interval Δt. If this clock moves with a velocity of $0.6c$, which of the following statements is *not* true?
   (a) the mass will be larger
   (b) the length will be shorter
   (c) the time interval will be longer
   (d) the time interval will be shorter

3. The rest mass of a proton is 1.673×10^{-27} kg. The relativistic mass of a proton when its velocity is $0.6c$ is approximately
   (a) 1.3×10^{-27} kg   (b) 2.1×10^{-27} kg
   (c) 2.6×10^{-27} kg   (d) 8.4×10^{-27} kg

4. What is the relativistic mass of an electron whose kinetic energy is 1.0 MeV?
   (a) 35.6 x 10^{-31} kg   (b) 29.2 x 10^{-31} kg
   (c) 26.9 x 10^{-31} kg   (d) 22.5 x 10^{-31} kg

5. According to the Bohr theory of an atom, an electron may circle the nucleus indefinitely without radiating energy if
   (a) the radius of its orbit is an integral multiple of the nuclear radius
   (b) its orbital path is an integral number of de Broglie wavelengths
   (c) if its orbit is an integral multiple of its angular momentum
   (d) the coulomb force is constant

6. What is the de Broglie wavelength of an electron when it is accelerated through a potential difference of 200 V?
   (a) 86.8 pm   (b) 62.2 pm   (c) 23.6 pm   (d) 6.92 pm

7. For the hydrogen atom, which of the following energy-level transitions will result in the emission of a photon with the greatest frequency?
   (a) from $n = 2$ to $n = 1$ (b) from $n = 1$ to $n = 4$
   (c) from $n = 4$ to $n = 2$ (d) from $n = 3$ to $n = 1$

8. The threshold frequency for a surface is known to be 5 x 10^{14} Hz. What is the wavelength of the light required to eject a photoelectron having a kinetic energy of 5 eV?
   (a) 120 nm   (b) 176 nm   (c) 211 nm   (d) 306 nm

9. The frequency of the first line in the Lyman series for hydrogen is found to be approximately
   (a) 2.47 x 10^{15} Hz   (b) 2.92 x 10^{15} Hz
   (c) 3.08 x 10^{15} Hz   (d) 3.29 x 10^{15} Hz

10. The energy of the photon emitted when an electron in the hydrogen atom drops from the $n = 3$ level to the $n = 2$ level is
    (a) 10.2 eV   (b) 6.8 eV   (c) 1.89 eV   (d) 1.51 eV

COMPLETION QUESTIONS

1. Einstein's first postulate tells us that there is no such thing as _____.

2. For objects traveling past an observer at relativistic speeds, the measurements of length are _____, the measurements of mass are _____, and the time intervals on the object are observed to be _____ than when at rest.

3. The _____ is constant for all observers independent of their state of motion. This statement is known as _____.

4. The maximum kinetic energy of an ejected photoelectron is equal to the difference between the _____ and _____.

5. The lowest energy level in an atom is known as its _____ state.

6. Electron jumps from higher quantum levels back to the first or lowest quantum level produce the _____ series for the hydrogen atom. Jumps back to the second level produce the _____ series.

7. If light from an incandescent platinum wire passes through sodium vapor before reaching the slit of a spectroscope, the resulting spectrum lacks the wavelength's characteristic of _____. Such a spectrum is known as an _____ spectrum.

8. The _____ is calculated by dividing Planck's constant by the product of the mass and velocity of a particle.

9. According to _____ first postulate, an electron may occupy only those orbits for which its angular momentum is an integral multiple of _____.

10. The minimum energy required to eject a photoelectron from a surface is known as the _____.

ANSWERS TO TRUE-FALSE, MULTIPLE CHOICE, AND COMPLETION QUESTIONS

1.	True	1.	c	1.	absolute rest
2.	False	2.	d	2.	shorter, larger, longer
3.	True	3.	b	3.	free-space velocity of photon,
4.	False	4.	c		Einstein's second postulate
5.	False	5.	b	4.	energy of the incident light,
6.	False	6.	a		work function of the surface
7.	False	7.	d	5.	ground
8.	True	8.	b	6.	Lyman, Balmer
9.	True	9.	a	7.	sodium vapor, absorption
10.	True	10.	c	8.	de Broglie wavelength
				9.	Bohr's, $h/2\pi$
				10.	work function

CHAPTER 42.   NUCLEAR PHYSICS AND THE NUCLEUS

CONTENTS

OBJECTIVES

You should be able to:

1. Discuss or write statements demonstrating an understanding of what is currently known about the mass, charge, and size of the fundamental nuclear particles.

2. Describe the current theory concerning the nuclear force as a mechanism for holding the nucleons together.

3. Define the mass number and the atomic number and give a relationship between them.

4. Demonstrate your understanding of the equivalence of mass and energy by interchanging units in kilograms, atomic mass units, joules, and electronvolts.

5. Define what is meant by an *isotope* and describe how the mass spectrometer is used to separate isotopes.

6. Calculate the mass defect and the binding energy per nucleon for a particular isotope.

7. Write a brief description of alpha particles, beta particles, and gamma rays, listing their properties.

8. Demonstrate your understanding of radioactive decay and nuclear reactions by writing nuclear equations for these events.

9. Calculate the activity and the quantity of a radioactive isotope remaining after a period of time if the half-life and the initial values are given.

10. Demonstrate your understanding of the various conservation laws as they apply to nuclear reactions.

11. Distinguish, by example and discussion, between *nuclear fission* and *nuclear fusion*.

12. Draw a rough diagram of a nuclear reactor describing the various components and their function in the production of electric power.

DEFINITIONS

<u>Nuclear force</u> - The fundamental, natural force which holds the nuclear particles together in the nucleus of an atom.

<u>Nucleon</u> - A general term applied to neutrons and protons, the constituent particles of an atomic nucleus.

<u>Atomic number</u> - A number used to identify elements. It is equal to the number of protons in the nucleus and is represented by the symbol Z.

<u>Mass number</u> - The total number of nucleons in an atomic nucleus. The mass number is the sum of the atomic number and the number of neutrons ($A = Z + N$).

<u>Atomic mass unit</u> - A unit of mass which is equal to one-twelfth the mass of the most abundant form of the carbon atom. Its value is equal to 1.6606×10^{-27} kg.

<u>Isotopes</u> - Atoms which have the same atomic number Z, but different mass numbers A.

<u>Mass spectrometer</u> - An instrument used to separate the isotopes of elements based on the differences in mass.

<u>Mass defect</u> - The difference between the rest mass of a nucleus and the sum of the rest masses of its constitutent nucleons.

<u>Binding energy</u> - The energy required to separate a nucleus into its constituent nucleons. It is an energy equivalent to the mass defect of an atom.

<u>Alpha particle</u> - The nucleus of a helium atom, which consists of two neutrons and two protons bound together by nuclear forces.

<u>Beta particle</u> - A beta minus particle is simply an electron. The beta plus particle has a mass equivalent to the electron, but its charge is equal and opposite to that of an electron.

<u>Activity</u> - The rate of distintegration of an unstable isotope. An activity of one curie is equivalent to 3.7×10^{10} disintegrations per second.

<u>Half-life</u> - The time in which one-half the unstable nuclei of a radioactive sample will decay.

<u>Nuclear reaction</u> - A process by which nuclei, radiation, and/or nucleons collide to form different nuclei, radiation, and/or nucleons.

<u>Conservation of charge</u> - The total charge of a system can neither be increased nor decreased in a nuclear reaction.

Conservation of nucleons - The total number of nucleons in a nuclear
reaction must remain unchanged.

Nuclear fission - The process by which heavy nuclei are split into two
or more nuclei of intermediate mass numbers.

Nuclear reactor - A device which controls the nuclear fission of
radioactive material producing new radioactive substances and
large amounts of energy.

Nuclear fusion - The process by which two lighter nuclei join together
to form a heavier nucleus.

PHYSICAL CONCEPTS

1. The fundamental nuclear particles discussed in this chapter are
    summarized in the following table. The masses are given in amu
    units and the charge is in terms of the electronic charge $+e$ or
    $-e$, which is 1.6×10^{-19} C.

    FUNDAMENTAL PARTICLES

Particle	Symbol	Mass, u	Charge
electron	$_{-1}^{0}e, _{-1}^{0}\beta$	0.00055	$-e$
proton	$_{1}^{1}p, _{1}^{1}H$	1.007276	$+e$
neutron	$_{0}^{1}n$	1.008665	0
positron	$_{+1}^{0}e, _{+1}^{0}\beta$	0.00055	$+e$
alpha particle	$_{2}^{4}\alpha, _{2}^{4}He$	4.001506	$+2e$

    The atomic masses of the various elements are given in the text.

2. The atomic number Z of an element is the number of protons in
    its nucleus. The mass number A is the sum of the atomic number
    and the number of neutrons N. These numbers are used to write
    the nuclear symbol:

    $$A = Z + N \qquad \text{symbol: } _{Z}^{A}X$$

3. One *atomic mass unit* (u) is equal to one-twelfth the mass of the
    most abundant carbon atom. Its value in kilograms is given below.
    Also, since $E = mc^2$, we can write the conversion factor from mass
    to energy as c^2.

$$1 \text{ u} = 1.6606 \times 10^{-27} \text{ kg} \qquad c^2 = 931 \text{ MeV/u}$$

$$1 \text{ MeV} = 10^6 \text{ eV} = 1.6 \times 10^{-13} \text{ J}$$

4. In the mass spectrometer, the velocity v and the radius R of the singly ionized particles are

$$v = \frac{E}{B} \qquad R = \frac{mv}{eB} \qquad \text{mass spectrometer}$$

5. The *mass defect* is the difference between the rest mass of a nucleus and the sum of the rest masses of its nucleons. The *binding energy* is obtained by multiplying the mass defect by c^2.

$$E_B = \left\{ [Zm_H + (A - Z)m_n] - M \right\} c^2 \qquad \text{binding energy}$$

where m_H = 1.007825 u
m_n = 1.008665 u
M = atomic mass
c^2 = 931 MeV/u

6. Several general equations for radioactive decay are

$$_Z^A X \rightarrow {}_{Z-2}^{A-4} Y + {}_2^4 \alpha + \text{energy} \qquad \text{alpha decay}$$

$$_Z^A X \rightarrow {}_{Z+1}^{A} Y + {}_{-1}^{0} \beta + \text{energy} \qquad \text{beta minus decay}$$

$$_Z^A X \rightarrow {}_{Z-1}^{A} Y + {}_{+1}^{0} \beta + \text{energy} \qquad \text{beta plus decay}$$

7. The *activity* R of a sample is the rate at which the radioactive nuclei decay. It is generally expressed in curies (Ci).

One curie (1 Ci) = 3.7 $\times$ 10^{10} *disintegrations per second* (s^{-1})

The *half-life* of a sample is the time $T_{\frac{1}{2}}$ in which one-half the unstable nuclei will decay.

8. The number of unstable nuclei remaining after a time t depends on the number n of half-lives that have passed. If N_0 nuclei exist at time t = 0, then a number N exists at time t. We have

$$N = N_0 \left(\tfrac{1}{2}\right)^n \qquad \text{where } n = \frac{t}{T_{\frac{1}{2}}}$$

The activity R and mass m of the radioactive portion of a sample are found from similar relations:

$$R = R_0 \left(\tfrac{1}{2}\right)^n \qquad m = m_i \left(\tfrac{1}{2}\right)^n$$

9. *In any nuclear equation, the number of nucleons on the left side must equal the number of nucleons on the right side. Similarly, the net charge must be the same on each side.*

TRUE-FALSE QUESTIONS

T   F   1.   The diameter of an atom is approximately 10,000 times the diameter of its nucleus.

T   F   2.   The difference between the mass number of an isotope and its atomic number is equal to the number of nucleons in the nucleus.

T   F   3.   An element may have more than one mass number, but the mass number for a stable isotope is fixed.

T   F   4.   The radioactive half-life of a substance is one-half of the time required for all of the unstable atoms in that substance to decay.

T   F   5.   In alpha decay, the mass number of an unstable isotope is reduced by 4 and the atomic number is reduced by 2.

T   F   6.   When $^{27}_{13}\text{Al}$ is bombarded by a neutron, the collision produces $^{27}_{12}\text{Mg}$ and a beta plus particle.

T   F   7.   The binding energy of an element is equivalent to the product of the mass defect and the square of the velocity of light.

T   F   8.   In a balanced nuclear equation the sum of the atomic numbers and the sum of the mass numbers must be the same on the two sides of the nuclear equation.

T   F   9.   In nuclear fission energy is emitted whereas in nuclear fusion energy is absorbed.

T   F   10. The function of the moderator in a nuclear reactor is to slow down the nuclear fission process and thereby control the release of energy.

MULTIPLE-CHOICE QUESTIONS

1. Isotopes are atoms which have the same
   (a) number of neutrons   (b) atomic number
   (c) number of nucleons   (d) atomic mass

2. The process by which a nucleus with a large mass number splits
   into lighter nuclei is called
   (a) fission   (b) fusion   (c) alpha decay (b) beta decay

3. In the mass spectrometer the distance from the slit to the impact
   on the plate is 10 cm for isotope A and 12 cm for isotope B.
   The ratio of their masses M_A/M_B is approximately
   (a) 0.83   (b) 0.93   (c) 1.2   (d) 1.33

4. If two light nuclei are fused together in a nuclear reaction,
   the average energy per nucleon
   (a) increases   (b) remains the same
   (c) decreases   (d) cannot be determined

5. A sample of radioactive material contains N radioactive nuclei
   at a given instant. If the half-life is 20 s, how many
   unstable nuclei remain after 1 h?
   (a) $N/2$ (b) $N/4$ (c) $N/6$ (d) $N/8$

6. Which of the following nuclear reactions is possible?

   (a) $_1^1H + {}_2^3He \rightarrow {}_2^4He$

   (b) $_2^4He + {}_{13}^{27}Al \rightarrow {}_{15}^{30}P + {}_0^1n$

   (c) $_1^2H + {}_{15}^{31}P \rightarrow {}_{13}^{29}Al + {}_2^4He$

   (d) $_{88}^{224}Ra \rightarrow {}_{86}^{219}Rn + {}_2^4He$

7. When a beta plus particle encounters an electron, they cancel one
   another out and both disappear. This *annihilation* of matter
   produces two photons, each having an energy of approximately
   (a) 0.466 MeV   (b) 0.511 MeV   (c) 0.931 MeV   (d) 1.02 MeV

8. A deuteron is a particle consisting of a neutron and a proton
   bound together by nuclear forces. If the rest mass of a
   deuteron is 3.34313×10^{-27} kg, the binding energy is approximately
   (a) 2.22 MeV   (b) 3.11 MeV   (c) 4.44 MeV   (d) 6.22 MeV

9. In a nuclear reactor, which of the following is used to slow
   down the fast neutrons released in the fission process?
   (a) the moderator   (b) the control rods
   (c) the radiation shielding   (d) the heat exchanger

10. The binding energy per nucleon for $_{92}^{235}U$, whose mass is
    235.043915 u, is approximately
    (a) 7.11 MeV   (b) 6.40 MeV   (c) 7.59 MeV   (d) 7.92 MeV

COMPLETION QUESTIONS

1. In general, the _____ is defined as the energy required to break up a nucleus into its constituent protons and neutrons.

2. When a proton bombards $^{27}_{13}Al$ in a nuclear reaction, the unstable nucleus _____ is formed, which finally results in the production of _____ and an alpha particle.

3. The half-life for alpha decay for deuterium is 10.2 s. One-fourth of the unstable atoms will remain after _____ s.

4. An activity of _____ is equal to 3.7×10^{10} disintegrations per second.

5. The _____ is the total number of nucleons in the nucleus and can be computed by adding the number of _____ to the number of _____ .

6. Basic components of a nuclear reactor are _____, _____, _____, _____, and _____ .

7. In nuclear fission, the fission fragments have a _____ mass number and hence a _____ binding energy per nucleon.

8. Isotopes are atoms which have the same _____ but different _____ .

9. A mass defect of 1 amu is equivalent to an energy of _____ .

10. Three quantities which must be conserved in a nuclear reaction are _____, _____, and _____ .

ANSWERS TO TRUE-FALSE, MULTIPLE CHOICE, AND COMPLETION QUESTIONS

1. True	1. b	1. binding energy
2. False	2. a	2. $^{28}_{14}Si$, $^{24}_{12}Mg$
3. True	3. a	
4. False	4. c	
5. True	5. d	3. 20.4
6. False	6. b	4. one curie
7. True	7. b	5. mass number, protons, neutrons
8. True	8. a	6. nuclear core, control rods,
9. False	9. a	heat exchanger, moderator,
10. False	10. c	radiation shielding
		7. smaller, larger
		8. atomic number, mass number
		9. 931 MeV
		10. charge, nucleons, energy

CHAPTER 43. ELECTRONICS

CONTENTS

OBJECTIVES

You should be able to:

1. Explain with the use of diagrams the operation of a vacuum-tube diode, a vacuum-tube triode, a cathode-ray tube, and an x-ray tube.

2. Describe what is meant by a *semiconductor*, using such concepts as *band theory, lattice structure,* and *impurities.*

3. Distinguish, by diagrams and discussion, between N- and P-type semiconductors, describing how they can be produced commercially by *doping.*

4. Describe, with figures, current flow across a PN junction under forward and reverse bias.

5. Explain how semiconductor diodes are used in the half-wave rectifier and the full-wave rectifier.

6. Demonstrate your understanding of the zener diode and its application.

7. Explain with the use of diagrams how a transistor operates when it is connected with a common base, a common emitter, and a common collector.

8. Solve problems similar to those in the text for transistor amplifiers.

9. Define and discuss the application of LEDs, photodiodes, silicon-controlled rectifiers, and integrated circuits.

DEFINITIONS

Thermionic emission - The emission of electrons from a solid body as a result of elevated temperature.

Diode - An electronic device consisting of two elements. In a vacuum tube these elements are the plate and the filament; in the semiconductor diode the two elements are formed by a PN junction.

Triode - An electronic device which consists of three elements. In a vacuum tube triode the elements are the plate, the filament, and the grid; the semiconductor triode may be an NPN or a PNP transistor.

Cathode-ray tube - An evacuated tube in which an electron beam is focused to a small cross section on a luminescent screen and can be varied in intensity and position to produce a pattern.

X-ray tube - A vacuum tube in which high energy electromagnetic rays (x-rays) are produced by bombarding a target with high-velocity electrons.

Semiconductor - A solid or liquid material with a resistivity between that of a conductor and an insulator.

Conduction band - A partially filled energy band in which electrons can move freely under the influence of a potential difference.

Donor - An impurity atom which tends to give up an electron to a material enhancing its semiconductor properties. Donors are used in producing N-type semiconductors.

Acceptor - An impurity atom which is deficient in valence electrons. When added to a semiconductor crystal it accepts an electron from a neighboring atom, leaving an electron hole in the lattice structure. Acceptors are used to produce P-type semiconductors.

N-type semiconductor - A semiconductor material consisting of donor impurities and free electrons.

P-type semiconductor - A semiconductor material consisting of acceptor atoms and electron holes.

PN junction - The union of a P-type crystal with an N-type crystal in such a way that current is conducted in only one direction.

Rectifier - An electronic device which has the property of converting alternating current into direct current.

Zener diode - A semiconductor device that exhibits a sudden rise in current if a certain reverse voltage is applied. If the diode is forward-biased, it acts as an ordinary rectifier. When reverse-biased, however, it exhibits a sharp break in its voltage-current graph.

Transistor - A semiconductor device consisting of three or more electrodes, usually the emitter, the collector, and the base.

<u>Integrated circuit</u> - A combination of interconnected circuit elements inseparably associated on or within a continuous material called a substrate.

PHYSICAL CONCEPTS

1. For a common-base transistor amplifier

   Emitter current = base current + collector current

   $$I_e = I_b + I_c \qquad \alpha = \frac{I_c}{I_e} \qquad \text{current gain}$$

2. The *current gain* for other connections is

   $$\beta = \frac{\alpha}{1 - \alpha} \qquad \text{common-emitter amplifier}$$

   $$A_i = \frac{1}{1 - \alpha} \qquad \text{common-collector amplifier}$$

3. The voltage gain A_v and the power gain G are given by

   $$A_v = \frac{V_{out}}{V_{in}} \qquad \text{voltage gain}$$

   $$G = \frac{power\ in}{power\ out} = \frac{V_{out}\ I_c}{V_{in}\ I_e}$$

   $$G = \alpha \frac{V_{out}}{V_{in}} = \alpha A_v \qquad \text{power gain}$$

TRUE-FALSE QUESTIONS

T F 1. Current flow in a vacuum-tube diode occurs only when the plate is negative with respect to the cathode.

T F 2. Semiconductors are materials in which the valence and conduction bands overlap.

T F 3. N-type semiconductors are produced by doping with donor atoms.

T F 4. For a reverse-biased PN junction, both holes and electrons move away from the junction and there is no current flow across the junction.

243

T   F   5.   PN junctions are semiconductor diodes and simple transistors are semiconductor triodes.

T   F   6.   The bridge rectifier uses four diodes to obtain half-wave rectification of alternating current.

T   F   7.   The zener diode is useful as a voltage-regulating device.

T   F   8.   In a transistor, the ratio of base current to emitter is sometimes referred to as current gain α.

T   F   9.   In a transistor amplifier the voltage gain is always greater than the power gain.

T   F   10.   The voltage gain is lowest for a common collector amplifier.

MULTIPLE-CHOICE QUESTIONS

1. A vacuum-tube triode amplifier in a radio circuit might be replaced in a miniature circuit by
   (a) a PN junction   (b) a zener diode
   (c) an NPN transistor   (d) a thermistor

2. Which of the following is not an application of diodes?
   (a) a filter   (b) bridge rectifier
   (c) full-wave rectifier   (d) half-wave rectifier

3. In an NPN transistor, the N-type part of the forward-biased section is called the
   (a) emitter   (b) collector   (c) base   (d) donor

4. A transistor for which $\alpha = 0.98$ has the following β value
   (a) 29   (b) 38   (c) 49   (d) 56

5. The amplifier circuit shown in the figure below is
   (a) a common-emitter amplifier
   (b) a common-base amplifier
   (c) a common-collector amplifier
   (d) none of these

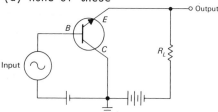

Fig. 43-1.

6. If $\alpha = 0.96$ for the arrangement in Figure 43-1, the current gain will be approximately
   (a) 0.96   (b) 1.06   (c) 24   (d) 25

7. Which of the following amplifier circuits acts as a signal inverter?
   (a) common emitter   (b) common collector
   (c) common base   (d) none of these

8. In a common-base amplifier circuit for which $\alpha = 0.98$ and the emitter current is 20 mA, the output resistance is 500 kΩ and the input resistance is 500 Ω. The voltage gain is approximately
   (a) 1000   (b) 1020   (c) 1040   (d) 1060

9. Which of the following electronic devices is used for digital displays in electronic calculators?
   (a) photodiodes   (b) zener diodes   (c) LEDs   (d) SRCs

10. Which of the following is *not* an indication of current gain in a transistor amplifier?
    (a) α (b) $\dfrac{\alpha}{1-\alpha}$ (c) $\dfrac{1}{1-\alpha}$ (d) $\dfrac{I_e}{I_c}$

COMPLETION QUESTIONS

1. The atom impurities used in producing N-type semiconductors are called _____ whereas P-type semiconductors are produced through doping with _____.

2. A PN junction is _____ biased when the positive terminal of a battery is connected to the P side and the negative terminal to the N side.

3. An electronic device which converts alternating current into direct current pulses in a manner that utilizes only half of the incoming signal is called _____.

4. A zener diode operating in the zener region of its characteristic curve will maintain a fairly constant _____ regardless of the current flow through it.

5. In a common base amplifier, the base current is equal to the difference between the _____ current and the _____ current.

6. The ratio of power gain G to voltage gain A_v is equal to _____.

7. The highest current gain is obtained with a common-_____ amplifier; the highest power gain is obtained with a common-_____ amplifier; and the highest voltage gain is obtained with a common-_____ amplifier.

8. The process of planting impurity atoms into semiconductor crystals is known as _____.

9. An electronic device which smooths out the pulses from a diode rectifier is called a _____.

10. A _____ is an electronic device that takes advantage of the fact that the resistance of a semiconductor decreases as the temperature decreases.

ANSWERS TO TRUE-FALSE, MULTIPLE CHOICE, AND COMPLETION QUESTIONS

1.	False	1.	c	1.	donors, acceptors
2.	False	2.	a	2.	forward
3.	True	3.	a	3.	a half-wave rectifier
4.	True	4.	c	4.	voltage
5.	True	5.	c	5.	emitter, collector
6.	False	6.	d	6.	α
7.	True	7.	a	7.	collector, emitter, base
8.	False	8.	b	8.	doping
9.	True	9.	c	9.	filter
10.	True	10.	d	10.	thermistor

PROBLEM SOLUTION

Problem solution in physics is usually a matter of recalling a
physical relationship between several parameters and applying it to
a given situation. However, proceeding from verbal statements to
mathematical symbols is often difficult for the beginning student.
A technique or standard approach to problem solving will often lead
to the proper equation when a careful reading does not immediately
suggest the solution. The following procedure is recommended:

1. Read the entire problem carefully and decide what
   physical concepts are involved.

2. Take one sentence at a time and translate the words
   into a diagram, labeling or listing all given data.
   All information contained in the problem should be
   represented in terms of diagrams, numbers, and
   symbols.

3. Indicate on the diagram, by an appropriate symbol
   and question mark, what you are asked to find or
   determine. (From now on you should not have to
   refer to the verbal problem again.)

4. Recall the physical principles which seem relevant
   to the problem. Express them concisely as an
   algebraic equation or formula.

5. Determine whether the given data are adequate to
   solve the problem. If not, decide what is missing
   and how to find it.

6. Decide whether the unknown quantity can be found
   more easily by direct substitution of numerical
   values or it would be better to solve algebraically
   before substitution.

7. Substitute the numerical values, including the
   number, sign, and proper units, for each known
   quantity. Solve for the value of the unknown and
   check its units for consistency.

An example of the proper approach to problem solution is given in
detail for the following example.

EXAMPLE: A force of 200 lb acts on a block at an angle of 30° above
the horizontal. Compute the work done by this force if it drags the
block for a horizontal distance of 20 ft.

Step 1. Read the problem and identify the concept of *work* as the
        basic principle involved.

Step 2. Draw each sentence and label knowns (see Fig. A-1).

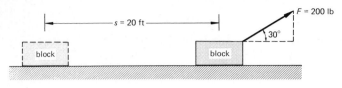

Fig. A-1.

<u>Step 3.</u> Indicate what is to be found. Note that all information is represented symbolically.

<u>Step 4.</u> Recall that *work* is the product of the displacement s and the component of force $F \cos \theta$ along the displacement. We write

$$\text{Work} = (F \cos \theta)s$$

<u>Step 5.</u> The data given for F, θ, and s are sufficient to solve for work.

<u>Step 6.</u> Direct substitution of numerical values is best in this instance.

<u>Step 7.</u> Solve for work by substitution.

$$\text{Work} = (F \cos \theta)s$$

$$= (200 \text{ lb}) (\cos 30°)(20 \text{ ft})$$

$$= (200 \text{ lb})(0.866)(20 \text{ ft})$$

$$= 3464 \text{ ft·lb}$$

NOTE: The unit ft·lb is appropriate for work, and the number is reasonable.

INDEX TO GLOSSARY TERMS

Thermal energy 83
Thermal equilibrium 83
Thermionic emission 241
Thermocouple 197
Thermodynamics 107
Thermoelectric effect 197
Thermometer 83
Threshold frequency 228
Throttling process 107
Time dilation 228
Torque 15
Torricelli's theorem 78
Torsion constant 66
Torsion pendulum 66
Total force 72
Total internal reflection 141
Trajectory 25
Transformer 214
Transistor 242
Transverse wave 113
Triode 242
Triple point 101
Turbulent flow 77

Ultimate strength 60
Ultrasonic 120
Ultraviolet radiation 126
Umbra 130
Uniform circular motion 44
Uniformly accelerated motion 21
Unit 3
Universal law of gravitation 45

Vaporization 89
Vector quantity 3
Velocity 21
Venturi effect 77
Vertex 136
Virtual image 136
Volt 171
Voltmeter 208

Water equivalent 89
Watt 35
Waveform 120
Wavelength 114
Wave motion 113
Wave speed 114
Weber 202
Weber per square meter 202
Weight 30
Weight density 72

Wheatstone bridge 189
Work 35
Work function 228

X-ray tube 242

Young's experiment 154
Young's modulus 60

Zener diode 242

RELATED DEPT.